Level **F**

FOCUS ON Reading Strategies

Perfection Learning®

Editorial Director: Susan C. Thies
Editor: Paula J. Reece
Writer: Jan Keese
Art Director: Randy Messer
Book Design: Deborah Lea Bell, Deb Yoder
Cover Design: Michael A. Aspengren

Reviewers:

Kathryn Black
Language Program Specialist
Mesa Public Schools
Mesa, Arizona

Cindy Brunswick
Literacy Coordinator
Center for School Improvement
University of Chicago
Chicago, Illinois

L. Michelle Johnson, M.Ed.
Education Department
Washington College
Chestertown, Maryland

Jan Keese
K–12 Reading Facilitator
Ankeny Community Schools
Ankeny, Iowa

Photo Credits: p. 6 ©Bettmann/CORBIS; p. 10 ©Bettmann/CORBIS;
p. 12 ©CORBIS; p. 15 ©CORBIS; p. 25 ©Bettmann/CORBIS; p. 52 ©Bettmann/CORBIS;
p. 125 ©Dallas and John Heaton/CORBIS

Some images www.clipart.com; www.photos.com; Corel Professional Photos;
Dynamic Graphics Liquid Library

For information, contact
Perfection Learning® Corporation
1000 North Second Avenue, P.O. Box 500
Logan, Iowa 51546-0500.
Phone: 1-800-831-4190
Fax: 1-800-543-2745
perfectionlearning.com

ISBN-10: 0-7891-6033-1
ISBN-13: 978-0-7891-6033-1

4 5 6 7 8 9 PP 13 12 11 10 09 08

Table of Contents

continued

Section 2

Unit 4: Make Inferences

Unit 5: Understand Characterization

Unit 6: Examine Theme

Lesson 1

The Lindbergh Baby Kidnapping

• *Narrative Nonfiction*

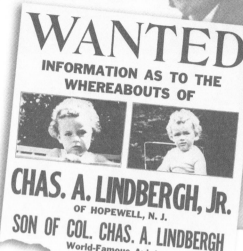

Heads Up You are about to read "The Lindbergh Baby Kidnapping." Think about questions you have just from reading the title. These are questions that you would hope to have answered as you read. For example, you're probably wondering "*Who or what is Lindbergh?*" What other questions do you have? Write them below.

Other Questions

_____

_____

_____

_____

The answers to these questions, which should be answered after you've read the text, are *relevant details*. Relevant details explain, support, or describe the featured topic or subject. Of course, there will be far more relevant details in the article than you can determine from the title.

As you read "The Lindbergh Baby Kidnapping," notice the Think-Along Questions throughout. Many will help you recognize the relevant details. Record your thoughts beside each Think-Along Question. Also, as you read, circle or highlight any words you don't know.

The Lindbergh Baby Kidnapping

by L. L. Owens

My Thoughts

1   On March 1, 1932, Charles and Anne Morrow Lindbergh's baby was kidnapped. He was taken from his crib in the family's Hopewell, New Jersey, home.

2   The world watched as the couple tried to get him back. The public mourned when he was found dead. And they rejoiced when Bruno Richard Hauptmann was convicted of the murder.

3   In the early 1930s, there were organized kidnapping rings. They had sprung up in every major U.S. city.

4   The criminals in these rings stole children. Then they demanded money from suffering parents. That money was called *ransom*. It was asked for in exchange for the child.

5   The wealthy were popular targets. And the Lindberghs were wealthy.

What questions do you have so far?

6   This baby's name was Charles A. Lindbergh Jr. He was 20 months old.

7   Anne put him to bed that night. He had a cold, so she made sure he was warm and comfortable. Anne left his side at 7:30 p.m.

8   The nursemaid was Betty Gow. She was still in the nursery when Anne left. She tidied up. She made sure the baby was covered. Then she opened a French window halfway.

9   Betty checked a short time later. The baby was fast asleep. The Lindberghs had dinner at about 8:30.

10   At 10:00, Betty entered the nursery. It was time for another routine check. She shut the window and turned on the heater.

Why are the times important details here?

11   Then she turned toward the crib. It was empty!

12   She quickly found Anne. She asked, "Do you have the baby, Mrs. Lindbergh?"

13   Anne did not.

14   "Perhaps Colonel Lindbergh has him then," said Betty.

continued

The Lindbergh Baby Kidnapping continued

15   The women searched the house. Charles didn't have the baby. None of the other servants had the baby. He was gone.

16   Charles examined the baby's room. The window was unlatched. It was open just a crack. A white envelope rested on the sill.

17   Charles didn't touch it. He knew it was a ransom note. And it was evidence.

18   He called the police at 10:25. Within 20 minutes, state law enforcement agencies had been notified. By 11:00, the investigation was well under way.

19   The police found four main pieces of evidence. The first was the ransom note. The second was an abandoned homemade ladder. The third was a shoe print in the mud near the ladder, and the fourth was a chisel near the ladder.

20   A rung on the ladder was broken. Police thought it had likely broken as the kidnapper came back down the ladder. So the kidnapper—with the baby—had probably fallen about five feet to the ground.

What prediction can you make about the baby?

21   The kidnapper clearly knew the layout of the house. And that person knew the schedule of the household. Police felt that more than one person had helped plan the crime.

22   The handwriting on the note was awkward. Experts thought the writer was probably Scandinavian. Or perhaps the writer was German. They decided this because of the placement of the dollar signs. Also, the spellings used showed that the writer didn't know English that well.

23   The Lindberghs were heartsick. Anne wrote letters to help her think through the situation. Charles tried to control the investigation. But both were helpless.

24   The public followed news of the case for the next several weeks. The Lindberghs received many fake ransom notes. Floods of mail from well-wishers also arrived.

25   Soon a meeting with the kidnapper was set up. A go-between delivered $50,000 to the supposed kidnapper.

26   In exchange, Charles received instructions. They told him where to find the baby. But the baby wasn't there.

27   On May 12, the couple's worst nightmare came true. The baby was found dead. He had been left in the woods just a few miles from home.

28   It appeared that he had died from a blow to the head. Police felt that he had been dead since the night he was taken. He may have even died in the fall from the ladder.

29   It was two years before an arrest was made.

30   Bruno Richard Hauptmann was a carpenter. And he was a German immigrant. He had entered the country illegally.

31   In September 1934, Hauptmann bought gas. He paid with a $10 gold certificate. This was an unusual way to pay.

32   The federal government first issued gold certificates in 1863. The paper currency notes were printed with orange ink. They were backed by 100 percent reserves of gold coin. They could be cashed in on demand. General use ended in 1933.

33   The gas station attendant noted Hauptmann's license number. And he took the certificate to the bank.

34   The bill was identified as part of the Lindbergh ransom money. Hauptmann was soon arrested.

35   Police found more ransom money in his garage. They also found the phone number of the Lindberghs' go-between. It was written on the wall in a closet.

List the details about the evidence against Hauptmann.

36   The trial was a major media event. The public watched with great interest. Everyone wanted justice for "Lucky Lindy," his beautiful wife, and their slain child.

What major media event can you think of that has happened during your lifetime?

37   Things went badly for Hauptmann. There was much **circumstantial** evidence against him. For one thing, he possessed some of the ransom money. Handwriting experts also testified that he had written the ransom notes. Also, the ladder was traced to him.

38   No witnesses placed Hauptmann at the scene of the crime. The footprint wasn't proven to be his. And his fingerprints were not found in the baby's room. They were not on the ransom notes either.

continued

The Lindbergh Baby Kidnapping continued

39   Still, he was found guilty. He was electrocuted April 3, 1936. The public felt that justice had been served.

40   As recently as 1992, Hauptmann's widow tried to clear his name. She believed her husband was framed. And his conviction should be overturned.

41   Some experts agree with Mrs. Hauptmann. They say that the case was mishandled, and it should be reopened.

> **What details support Hauptmann's innocence?**

42   So far, the courts have been unwilling to take another look.

43   One thing seems clear, though. The Lindbergh baby case will go down in history as one of the most famous kidnappings.

Make Sense of Words What happens when you are reading and you come to a word that you do not know? Do you skip over it, stop reading the selection altogether, or try to figure out its meaning? Authors choose their words carefully, and chances are, you will understand a selection or an author's perspective more fully if you take the time to get acquainted with the strange new word.

One way to help figure out a word's meaning is by looking for clues in the sentences surrounding the word. These are called *context clues*. Sometimes the clue is actually a definition or an explanation in simpler terms (**definition clue**). This is the most helpful type of context clue! However, other types of context clues can also put you on the right track to understanding. Sometimes writers give familiar examples of the unfamiliar word (**example clue**). This will give you a good idea about the word's meaning. Other times, writers give examples of what the word is *not* like. Instead, they include a situation that represents the *opposite* meaning (**contrast clue**). Yet other times, writers include a description that modifies the challenging word (**description clue**).

Look for the bolded word in paragraph 37 of "The Lindbergh Baby Kidnapping." Read the sentences surrounding the word, looking for context clues that can help you determine the challenging word's definition. Fill in the chart below.

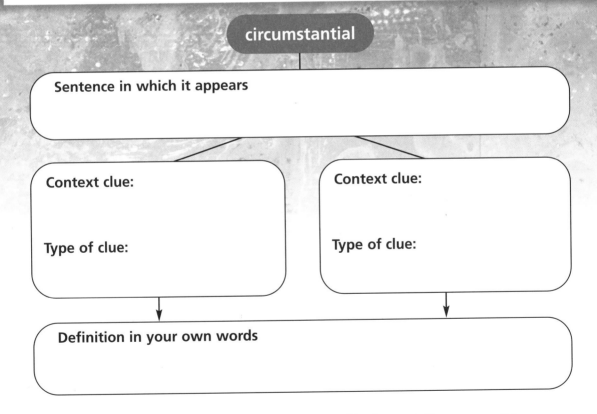

circumstantial

Sentence in which it appears

Context clue:

Type of clue:

Context clue:

Type of clue:

Definition in your own words

Now look back at the other words you marked in the text. Can you use this vocabulary strategy to help you figure out the meanings of those words?

Read with Understanding Were the questions you wrote before reading "The Lindbergh Baby Kidnapping" answered? Were the answers to your questions *relevant details*? Since this article features the kidnapping of Charles and Anne Lindbergh's infant son, the relevant details should be facts that help you understand that event. Look at the details listed below. These details were not in the article you just read, but they all relate to the Lindberghs. Choose the detail that would be the *least* relevant to this article.

① Charles Lindbergh made his first solo nonstop flight across the Atlantic Ocean on May 20–21, 1927.

② The "Lindbergh Law" made kidnapping a federal crime if the mail service is used to demand a ransom.

③ Bruno Richard Hauptmann was a carpenter by trade.

④ Charles Lindbergh demanded to lead the investigation into the kidnapping himself.

Understand by Seeing It *Relevant details* support the featured topic or subject. The arrest and conviction of Bruno Richard Hauptmann was an important event of the Lindbergh baby kidnapping. Use the organizer below to list the relevant details from the article that supported the arrest and conviction of Hauptmann.

Bruno Richard Hauptmann was arrested and convicted of kidnapping the Lindbergh baby.

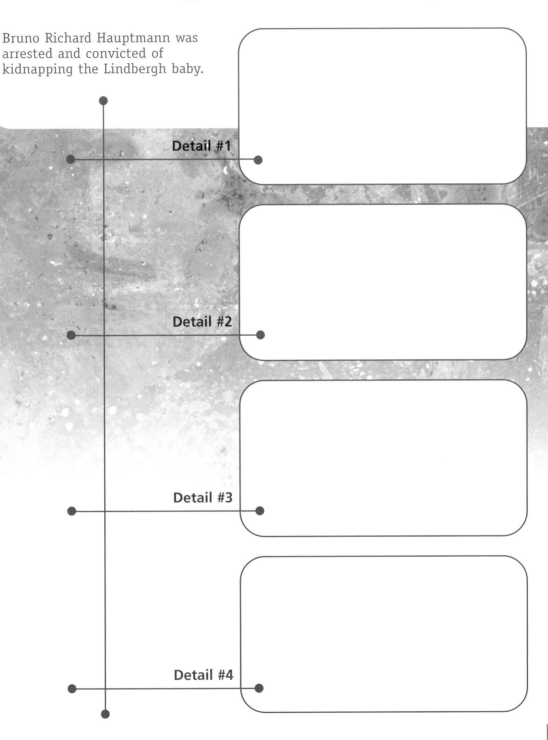

Detail #1

Detail #2

Detail #3

Detail #4

Write to Learn Imagine you are a newspaper reporter. Use the chart you created on page 13 to write a short article informing your readers of the details behind the arrest and conviction of the Lindbergh baby kidnapper. You may include a headline for your article.

Lesson 2

The Hilo and Aleutian
Tsunami

• *Narrative Nonfiction*

Heads Up You are about to read a narrative text called "The Hilo and Aleutian Tsunami." The author based this on a story told by Laura Chock about her experiences and actual events that occurred on April 1, 1946. Titles give you clues about what you are going to be reading. In order to begin the reading with some background knowledge and understanding, you must understand the vocabulary words included in the title.

In this title, both *Hilo* and *Aleutian* refer to places. Hilo is a city in Hawaii, and the Aleutian Islands are near Alaska. You are likely wondering what connection a city in Hawaii would have with islands in Alaska. If you know what a tsunami is, you might be able to predict what the connection is between these two locations. In the space provided on the next page, write your prediction of how Hilo and the Aleutian Islands might be connected, including your best guess at what a tsunami is and how it relates to these two locations.

continued

My Predictions

_____

_____

_____

_____

_____

_____

_____

_____

_____

You should find the answers to these predictions as you read. Remember, a prediction is your best guess based on the information you have at the time. You will find *relevant details* as you read that will answer your questions, explain the connection between Hilo and the Aleutian Islands, and confirm or deny your predictions.

As you read "The Hilo and Aleutian Tsunami," notice the Think-Along Questions throughout. Record your thoughts. Also, as you read, circle or highlight any words you don't know.

The Hilo and Aleutian
Tsunami

by Sarah Beth Cavanah

1   Laura Chock woke up quickly. Something was wrong.

2   The 18-year-old girl didn't take the time to put on clothes. She went downstairs to her parents' shop still wearing her pajamas.

3   Laura knew many Americans thought she lived in paradise. But Hawaii could be as dangerous as it was beautiful. Less than five years earlier, the Japanese had bombed Pearl Harbor, Hawaii. Many people had died, and many American ships were destroyed. The bombing had caused the United States to join World War II.

4   The war was supposed to be over. But what if it wasn't? What if the Japanese were back?

> What clues or details does the author provide that perhaps something bad is happening?

5   But when Laura made it downstairs to the chicken shop, she didn't see fire and destruction from bombs. Instead, she found herself standing in water up to her knees. Laura and her family looked around. It wasn't the war, but it was still dangerous.

6   Outside, children were playing in the flooded streets. They were screaming with delight. To them, the water seemed like a great new toy. They didn't know what was coming.

7   Suddenly, a wave of water 5 feet high crashed through the doors and windows of the store. Laura and her family raced up the stairs. They avoided drowning, but the chickens in their cages weren't so lucky.

8   Laura and her family waited for the water to go back down. Then they quickly ran downstairs and out into the street. The family was trying to move inland. They didn't want to be caught in another wave.

> Why would they want to move inland?

continued

9   Laura struggled to carry her five-year-old sister. Two more children held on to her as they tried to move as quickly as they could through the knee-deep water. The strong tug of the water ripped off Laura's shoes and one of her pajama legs. But there was no time to stop.

10   Laura noticed that the children were still screaming. But now they were screaming in fear.

> How might Laura know the screaming had changed from delight to fear?

11   Finally, Laura and her family made it to dry and high ground. Many people stood in the street looking around at one another and down toward the shore. Children were asking their parents what had happened. The adults knew. It was a tsunami, a huge wave that destroys everything in its path.

> What is a tsunami?

12   "Why didn't someone tell us it was coming?" a child asked. But the answer was that no one knew.

Birth of a Tsunami

13   The tsunami that rushed through Laura's family's shop had started thousands of miles away. It was just after midnight on April Fool's Day in 1946. An earthquake was shaking the ocean floor near the Aleutian Islands in the state of Alaska.

14   Nature was playing an April Fool's Day joke. No one could feel an earthquake on the ocean floor. So how would they even know it happened?

15   But this was no joke. Ocean earthquakes aren't dangerous for the shaking, but for what the shaking causes. The violent action of the earthquake pushes the water.

16   Think about what happens when someone jumps into a swimming pool. The **force** from the body causes the water to move. After a while, the waves reach the far end of the pool. Not a big deal, right? Now imagine hundreds of people jumping into the pool at once. The force would be much stronger, causing the waves at the end of the pool to be much bigger as well. This is similar to what happens with a tsunami.

17   Hawaii wasn't the only place to feel the force of the tsunami. On the Alaskan island of Unimak, five men lost their lives.

18   The men were working at the Scotch Cap Lighthouse on the island. Their job was to warn ships in the dark to avoid the rocky areas around the island. But they didn't get enough warning about the tsunami headed their way.

19   A wave nearly 100 feet high crashed into the lighthouse. It swept the men away and threw them onto the hard rocky ground.

20   Just like a person jumping into the middle of a pool, the wave spread in all directions. Strangely, tsunamis are only dangerous to people on land. While out in the ocean, the tsunami is almost invisible.

21   While at sea, the waves are only a few feet high and usually more than 100 miles apart. Ships sail right over the waves, and airplanes flying over cannot see them. But the waves move quickly, 600 miles per hour or more.

22   When the water gets shallower, the waves slow down. They start to grow larger and larger and closer together. Six hours after the earthquake, waves traveling 30 miles an hour and 100 feet high crashed into Hilo, Hawaii.

No Warning

23   Even though a tsunami had hit Alaska hours before, no one in Hawaii knew what was coming. James U. C. Low was driving in his car. When he looked toward the shore, he couldn't believe his eyes. A great wall of water was coming toward him from the bay. It was like nothing he had ever seen.

Why wouldn't the people in Hilo, Hawaii, know the tsunami was coming?

24   James didn't know what to do. He drove toward a gas station. He thought he could take shelter inside. But by the time he got to the station, the wave had gotten to him. The water rushed through the windows and the joints in the car.

What do you think James will do?

continued

The Hilo and Aleutian Tsunami continued

25   James suddenly found himself neck-deep in water and frozen in fear. James might not have been moving, but his car was. The wave was pushing the whole car, with James in it. The spell was broken. James jumped out the window and escaped.

26   The first wave hit as students and teachers at Laupahoehoe School were preparing to begin the day. Masuo Kino was outside the school when the wave hit. It picked him up and flipped him over.

27   Masuo had no control. The wave was carrying him toward a rock wall that ran around the area of the school. Masuo thought, "I'm going to die. I'm going to hit headfirst into that rock wall, and I'm going to die."

28   There was nothing Masuo could do. The water shot him toward the wall. Then, just before he hit, another part of the wave hit the wall. The wall collapsed and Masuo was saved. Instead of going headfirst into a solid wall, Masuo was pushed along with the pieces of the broken wall.

What is the most frightening situation you've experienced?

29   Sixteen students and five teachers were killed at Laupahoehoe School. Overall, 159 Hawaiians died from the tsunami.

30   No one wanted to be caught with no warning again. The American government developed a system to warn people that tsunamis were coming. They set up the Pacific Tsunami Warning System in Honolulu, Hawaii, to watch for events that could cause a tsunami. The center puts out "tsunami watches" that are like thunderstorm or tornado watches in mainland America.

31   Laura's chicken shop survived the 1946 tsunami. It was later destroyed in another tsunami in 1960. But thanks to better warning, no tsunami in Hawaii has ever been as deadly as the one Laura survived in 1946.

Make Sense of Words Authors choose words to make their writing communicate what is important. They might choose technical words that are needed for you to understand certain concepts. They might choose colorful words to help create a picture or feeling. They might choose words that are consistent with the style of writing they are using. Whatever the reason, the words may or may not be words that you know. There are a variety of strategies to determine the meaning of these unfamiliar words.

Sometimes authors clearly and specifically define a word right in the text. An example of this would be with the word **tsunami**. The sentence from the text says, "It was a **tsunami**, a huge wave that destroys everything in its path." This sentence states the specific word, **tsunami**, and then directly states the meaning, "a huge wave that destroys everything in its path."

At other times the author chooses words and assumes that you have a basic understanding of them or can find clues about them within the text.

Complete the chart below for the word **force** found in paragraph 16. You are probably familiar with this word but may not have thought about it the way it is used in this specific context.

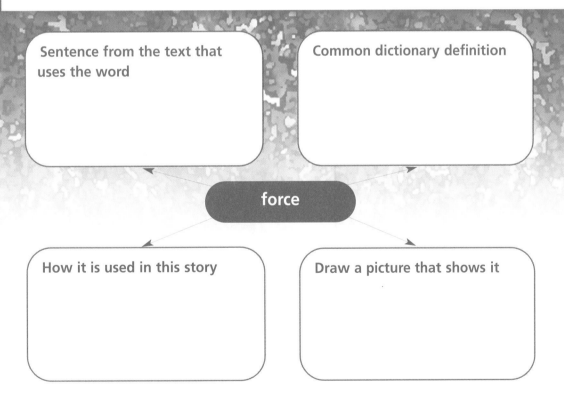

Sentence from the text that uses the word	Common dictionary definition

force

How it is used in this story	Draw a picture that shows it

Now look back at the other words you marked in the text. Can you use this vocabulary strategy to help you figure out the meanings of those words?

Read with Understanding What did you find out about your predictions as you read this essay? Did you have any idea what a tsunami was? Were you able to make any connection between Hilo and the Aleutian Islands? Were you able to locate *relevant details* that helped you determine the accuracy of your predictions or your understanding of the main idea? Look at the details listed below. Choose the detail that you would predict to be true based on your understanding of what a tsunami is.

① You are most likely to personally experience a tsunami if you live in the central part of the United States.

② Because we understand what causes tsunamis, another one will never occur.

③ You could experience a tsunami if you lived on the East Coast of the United States.

④ No lives will ever be lost again from a tsunami.

Understand by Seeing It This essay told the story of Laura Chock and the experiences of people in Hilo as they faced a tsunami. It also shared many facts about tsunamis, explaining what they are and what can cause them. Complete the chart below by organizing the *relevant details* about tsunamis as they relate to the two categories.

Relevant details as they describe the experiences of people in Hawaii during the April 1, 1946, tsunami

1._____

_____

_____

2._____

_____

_____

3._____

_____

_____

4._____

_____

_____

5._____

_____

_____

Relevant details as they describe what tsunamis are and what causes them

1._____

_____

_____

2._____

_____

_____

3._____

_____

_____

4._____

_____

_____

5._____

_____

_____

Lesson 3

The U.S. Olympic Hockey Team: 1980

• *Expository Nonfiction*

Heads Up You are about to read an article titled "The U.S. Olympic Hockey Team: 1980." The year 1980 was before you were born, but you may have some experience with the Olympics or hockey. You may also have some ideas about the 1980s based on what you've read, what someone has told you, or movies you have watched that take place during that decade. To activate and organize your prior knowledge, brainstorm and list words that connect to hockey, the Olympics, or the 1980s in the chart on the next page. A couple of examples are provided for you.

continued

A	B	C	D	E
F	G **gold medal**	H **hockey stick**	I	J
K	L	M	N	O
P	Q	R	S	T
U	V	W	X	Y
Z				

After reading the essay, you will be working on the skill of *summarizing*. Being able to take a passage you've read and condense it into a couple of sentences or a short paragraph will help you better understand what you have read. Summarizing requires you to think about the text, determine what is important, and then share that condensed information. As you read, use the Think-Along Questions to help focus your thinking. Record your thoughts beside each. Also, as you read, circle or highlight any words you don't know.

The U.S. Olympic Hockey Team: 1980

by Joanne and James Mattern

1   In 1980, America badly needed something to cheer about. Seventy-nine Americans were being held hostage in Iran. The price of everything was up. Many people were unemployed. The U.S. government was angry at the Soviet government for invading the small country of Afghanistan.

> Can you describe in one sentence why Americans needed something to cheer about in 1980?

2   The U.S. Olympic Committee was even considering a **boycott** of the 1980 Summer Olympics. The Games were to be held in Moscow, the Soviet Union's capital city.

3   In those dark days of February 1980, American athletes gathered in the tiny village of Lake Placid, New York, to compete in the Winter Olympic Games. No one expected the United States to do very well at the Games. The Soviets, on the other hand, were expected to win a lot of medals.

> Why might no one think the U.S. team would do well?

4   One gold medal the Soviets were sure to win was in hockey. Since 1964, the Soviets had won every Olympic hockey gold medal.

5   The American team was given little chance of winning any medals. The team was a collection of college and minor-league players coached by Herb Brooks. He was the hockey coach at the University of Minnesota.

6   But Herb Brooks and his **ragtag** team had other plans.

7   When he signed on as the hockey team's coach, Brooks knew he had a lot of work ahead of him. He had to take a group of confident, stubborn young men and teach them how to work together as a team. If his players weren't as naturally talented as the Soviets, Brooks was determined they would work twice as hard to make up for it.

continued

The U.S. Olympic Hockey Team: 1980 continued

8   Brooks had his players skate up and down the ice to build up their stamina and speed. He made them run as if they were training for a track-and-field event instead of a hockey game. And he didn't give anyone a break, no matter how tired the player was. Herb Brooks was one tough coach.

9   Training wasn't the only way Brooks got his team ready for the Olympics. The team played a series of 61 exhibition games. They played all sorts of teams—college, foreign, and National Hockey League (NHL) teams.

> What would be the value in playing such a variety of teams?

10   The Americans won 42 games. That should have made them pretty confident. But in the last game of the tour, the Americans faced the Soviets. They lost by the embarrassing score of 10 to 3. Everyone expected the same thing to happen during the Olympics.

11   The Americans finally arrived at Lake Placid. They had been training and playing together for six months. They were friends and teammates. But they still weren't great hockey players. In fact, the team was ranked seventh out of the 12 Olympic teams.

12   The teams were divided into two divisions. The Americans' first game was against Sweden. Only a few thousand people came to watch.

13   The Americans trailed through most of the game. But the team came back to end up with a tie. Even though they didn't win, the Americans were pleased with this result. It proved that they could come from behind and not give up.

14   Next, the U.S. team faced Czechoslovakia. Once again, the Czechs took an early lead. But America's Mike Eruzione scored a goal to tie the game with $4\frac{1}{2}$ minutes left in the first period.

15   After that, there was no stopping the United States. They went on to win—and win big—by a score of 7 to 3.

16   Suddenly, the Americans—whom everyone had expected to be **eliminated** by then—were tied with Sweden for first place in their division.

17   Hockey fans were beginning to notice the American team. Instead of being half-filled, the Olympic Ice Arena was packed for their next three games. And the United States didn't disappoint their fans. They beat Norway 5 to 1, Romania 7 to 2, and West Germany 4 to 2.

18   The Americans ended that first round with a record of 4–0–1. That was good enough to move on to the medal round.

19   America's first **opponent** in the medal round was the dreaded Soviets. The two teams faced off against each other on February 22, 1980. The Soviets had breezed through their division, winning all five games. They would be a mighty **foe**.

> Predict how the U.S. team will do against the Soviets.

20   But surprisingly, the U.S. hockey players weren't scared to face the mighty Soviet team. Goalie Jim Craig summed up the team's feelings when he said that they were eager to get a shot at the team. Coach Brooks encouraged this attitude by making jokes about the Soviet players. Doing this meant his team wouldn't take their opponents too seriously.

21   As usual, the Americans fell behind early in the game, 2 to 1. Then, with just one second left in the first period, American Mark Johnson slipped a shot past the Soviet goalie. The score was tied.

22   The second period was 20 minutes of tough, physical hockey. The Soviets outshot the Americans, 12 to 2. Amazingly, goalie Craig blocked all but one of those shots. Still, the Soviets were leading 3 to 2 when the teams came out for the third, and last, period.

23   Over 10,000 fans in the Olympic Ice Arena began to chant, "U.S.A! U.S.A!" Their chants turned to cheers when Mark Johnson scored his second goal of the game to tie the score again.

24   Then, a little over a minute later, the U.S. team's captain, Mike Eruzione, slammed the puck into the net from 30 feet away.

25   The crowd—and the team—went wild. Eruzione was **mobbed** by his joyful teammates. The Americans weren't just winning, they were winning against the "unbeatable" Soviets!

continued

The U.S. Olympic Hockey Team: 1980 continued

26   Ten minutes of play still remained. But the heart seemed to have gone out of the Soviet players. They played sloppily. They skated slowly and took wild shots at the American goal. Jim Craig had no trouble blocking those shots and protecting the U.S. team's lead.

What might the authors mean when they say, "the heart seemed to have gone out of the Soviet players"?

27   The crowd exploded with cheers as the last few seconds ticked off the clock. The spectators waved American flags over their heads. And the entire U.S. team crowded onto the ice, hugging one another and throwing their sticks into the air.

28   Above it all, television announcer Al Michaels screamed, "Do you believe in miracles? Yes!"

29   The joy of victory spread out of the Olympic Ice Arena and all over the country. People honked their car horns. They cried. They danced in the streets. Total strangers hugged one another and sang the national anthem. Suddenly, the dark cloud that had covered the United States was broken by a beam of light.

30   The only person not sharing in the celebration was Herb Brooks. He was thrilled at what his players had accomplished. But he remembered the one thing everyone else seemed to have forgotten. The Americans hadn't won any medals yet. They still had one more game to play. It was to be against a strong team from Finland. The winner of that game would go home with the gold medal.

31   Two days after their incredible victory against the Soviet Union, the Americans were back on the ice to face Finland. Once again, they quickly fell behind, 1 to 0.

32   Each team scored a goal in the second period. But in the third period, the United States scored three straight goals to put the game away. The final score was the United States 4, Finland 2. The U.S. hockey team had won the gold medal! Once again, a delighted crowd chanted "U.S.A! U.S.A!"

33   During the medal ceremony that followed the game, team captain Mike Eruzione stood alone at the top of the platform to sing the national anthem. But as soon as the music finished playing, he waved at his teammates to join him on the platform. A group of underdogs had come together as a team to beat the odds and show the world that miracles really do happen.

> Describe a time in your life when you "beat the odds" to accomplish something others didn't think you could.

Make Sense of Words Sometimes an author chooses a word because it is necessary for understanding the *content*. Other times, the author might choose a word because of what it adds to the *style* of the text. Read the six words listed below. Return to the story and reread each sentence where the words are found. Record each sentence in the chart below. Then write whether you think the word is important for understanding the content or whether it is used for style. Finally, explain your answer. If you are not sure of the meaning of a word, you may use the dictionary. An example has been completed for you.

Word	Sentence	Content or Style	Explain Your Answer
boycott (¶2)	"The U.S. Olympic Committee was even considering a **boycott** of the 1980 Summer Olympics."	Content	Helps the reader understand that not even the upcoming Olympics offered Americans much to look forward to
ragtag (¶6)			
eliminated (¶16)			
opponent (¶19)			
foe (¶19)			
mobbed (¶25)			

Now look back at the other words you marked in the text. Can you use this vocabulary strategy to help you figure out the meanings of those words?

Read with Understanding If you had to determine just one sentence that best *summarizes* the essay, which would you choose?

① The 1980 Winter Olympics was a fun Olympics for the hockey team from the Soviet Union.

② Hockey is a great sport in countries all over the world.

③ The year 1980 was a difficult year for everyone involved in hockey.

④ The U.S. Olympic hockey team's success showed that hard work pays off.

Understand by Seeing It When you *summarize*, you are selecting what you think are the most important pieces of information to retell. Summarizing is not telling every little detail that happened, but selecting the most important information needed to help someone else understand what you read. Complete the following graphic organizer about "The U.S. Olympic Hockey Team: 1980."

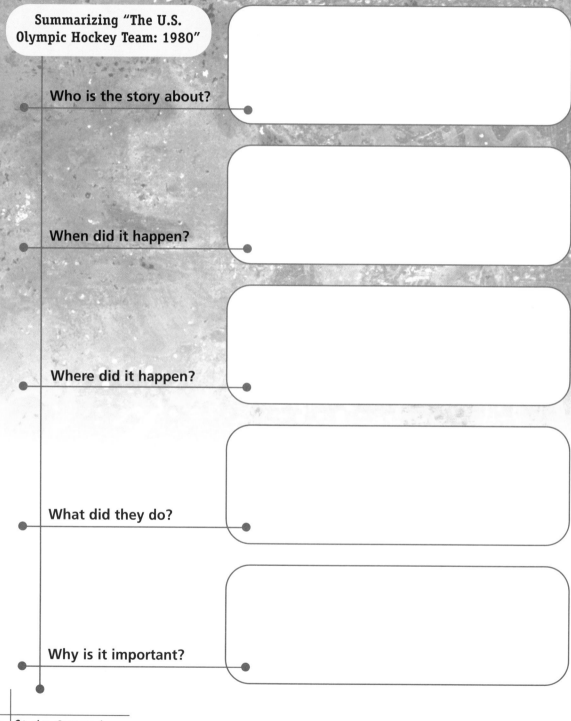

Summarizing "The U.S. Olympic Hockey Team: 1980"

Who is the story about?

When did it happen?

Where did it happen?

What did they do?

Why is it important?

Pretend that you are a sportscaster for a local TV station. Using the information in the graphic organizer you just completed, write a summary of the essay that could be read on your sports segment of the local newscast. Remember, you want to share the most important information but not retell every detail.

Lesson 4

The Old Rooster and Why He Scratches

• *African American Folktale*

Heads Up Building background knowledge and calling up prior knowledge help focus your thinking prior to reading. These valuable strategies enrich understanding while you read and can be accomplished a variety of ways. The folktale "The Old Rooster and Why He Scratches" contains some words you may not be familiar with. Some of these words are sorted by part of speech and listed below.

Noun	Adjective	Verb	Adverb
nuisance	delectable	cater	sincerely
banquet	ornery	adorned	furiously
repast	paltry	stalked	
	collective	flourishing	
		scurrying	
		mutters	

Reviewing the words before reading helps you build background knowledge, and using the words in a variety of ways enhances that background knowledge. First, look up the meaning of any words you don't know. Then create a variety of sentences from the words that you think could relate to the folktale. You may use more than one word per sentence, if you wish. Based on these sentences, can you predict what you think the folktale might be about?

My Sentences

_____

_____

_____

_____

_____

My Prediction

Use the Think-Along Questions to help focus your thinking while you are reading. Record your thoughts beside each. Pay attention to how you can use the strategy of *summarizing* to be a more active reader. Also, as you read, circle or highlight any words you don't know.

The Old Rooster
and Why He Scratches

retold by David Haynes

1   All the animals had been working hard at their various jobs. So to celebrate, they decided to get together and have a big feast. Since they were too tired to cook, they called their favorite restaurant. It was the only one in town that served foods everyone liked. The owner of the restaurant said that he'd be glad to cater the party. In fact, he would create a special dinner that would surprise and delight each and every one.

2   The feast was held in the town hall that night. When the animals arrived, they couldn't believe their eyes. Each table was adorned with steaming mounds of golden food. The animals rushed to their places to inspect the delectable food more closely. They oohed and aahed when they realized the golden mounds were actually buttery corn bread, fresh and oven-hot!

> The caterer said he would serve foods that every animal liked. Do you think all the animals like corn bread?

3   "Let's dig in," everyone cried.

4   Everyone, that is, except Rooster.

> Predict why Rooster didn't dig in.

5   Now, Rooster is known about these parts as a tough sort of fellow to get along with. To begin with, he's an early riser. And he feels everyone else should get up when he does. So, while the sheep, the goats, and the rest of the animals are still enjoying their sweet rest, here he comes. And just before the sun stretches its arms into the horizon, Rooster disturbs the peace with his cock-a-doodle-doo.

> Are you an early riser or a late sleeper?

6   Sometimes Rooster acts like he owns the barnyard. Why, no one can just innocently stroll through, minding his own business. Rooster is always there, pecking around the person's feet. The rooster makes such a nuisance of himself

that finally it gets to where decent folks don't want to be around him.

What reasons can you give for why the rooster thinks he owns the barnyard?

7   Now, despite all that, the animals had still invited the rooster to the feast. They knew that though he was ornery, he had never been lazy. Still, none of them expected the display of bad manners that Rooster provided.

8   "What's up with this food?" crowed the rooster.

9   "You have a problem with it?" asked Sister Hen sincerely. She was known by all to be a **peacemaker**. So naturally, she would try to keep the evening from being ruined.

10   "Problem!" crowed the rooster. "Am I the only one here who sees the problem? Look at this food. Why it's nothing but corn bread!"

Do you think the rooster was the only one who had noticed it was only corn bread? Why or why not?

11   "I'm sure you'll find—" started Sister Hen, but the rooster cut her off before she could finish.

12   "Corn bread here," crowed the rooster, pointing to one table. "And here," he said, pointing to another, "and here. Corn bread as far as the eye can see. I can get plenty of corn bread at home, thank you very much. I'll not stay around for this paltry meal."

13   With that, the rooster stalked from the room, flourishing his tail feathers behind him. Some of the animals stared after him, gape-mouthed. However, many of them were pleased that the old complainer had left. All the fussing would be over, and there would be even more food left for those who remained.

Summarize Rooster's behavior at the feast.

14   Everyone dug in, plucking the still-steaming corn bread from heaping platters. But an even bigger surprise was awaiting the animals. What do you think they found buried under the corn bread? Why, every tasty dish you could

continued

The Old Rooster and Why He Scratches continued

imagine, that's what. There was pizza, barbecued ribs, onion rings, cheesecakes, cherry pies, lemon pies, and apple pies. Everyone's favorite dish was hidden under one of the piles of corn bread. The owner of the restaurant had kept his word. He'd made a meal to surprise and delight everyone.

15   A collective cry of joy arose from the animals as they uncovered the secret dishes. The loud cries brought the rooster scurrying back to see what he was missing. You see, he was as nosy as he was ornery. When he saw the repast that had been uncovered, he sputtered with anger.

16   "How could I have been fooled by that silly chef?" he asked himself disgustedly. But his pride kept him from rejoining the group, although the other animals surely would not have minded. Instead, old Rooster crept back to his home, missing what was perhaps the best banquet of his life.

Why would "pride" keep Rooster from joining the group?

17   Poor Rooster. If only he had learned that things are not always as they appear. No one had ever taught him that patience is often rewarded.

When has patience rewarded you or someone you know?

18   That feast did teach the old rooster one lesson, however. The old bird still struts around the barnyard, but if you watch him for a while, you'll see something else. Every so often, he scratches the ground, digging down into the dirt. It looks like he's scratching for something hidden beneath the soil. And around suppertime, he scratches furiously, going after every little grain of corn.

19   "One of these days I'll find a feast," he mutters. "One of these days."

Make Sense of Words When you come across an unknown word, or sometimes even a word you might be familiar with, you can help determine the meaning by *rereading* the sentence the word is in. However, sometimes *reading on* will also provide clues to a word's meaning. This strategy can often help you determine the meaning of the unknown word or determine the specific meaning intended within the context of the story for a familiar word. *Rereading* the sentence containing the term and *reading on* are both strategies to help determine a word's meaning by using *context clues*. In paragraph 9, find the word **peacemaker**. Reread the sentence that contains the word. Then read on to see if you find more context clues. Finally, complete the graphic organizer below. Remember, *synonyms* are words with the same or similar meanings, and *antonyms* are words with opposite meanings. Determining synonyms and antonyms for **peacemaker** will help you better understand its meaning.

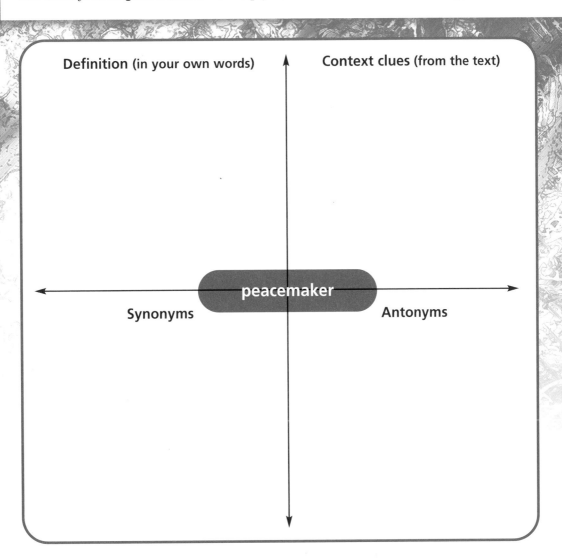

Now look back at the other words you marked in the text. Can you use this vocabulary strategy to help you figure out the meanings of those words?

Read with Understanding Before reading, you previewed vocabulary words from the folktale, created a variety of sentences, and predicted what the tale might be about. The vocabulary word you just worked with was **peacemaker**. After thinking about this vocabulary word and completing the graphic organizer on page 41, select the sentence you think would be the most accurate about Sister Hen.

① Sister Hen did not like conflict.

② Sister Hen did not like Rooster.

③ Sister Hen was the oldest member of the barnyard.

④ Sister Hen had a lot of pride.

Understand by Seeing It

Summarizing the whole story requires that you read the text for the important information or the main idea and then organize that into a brief form. Summarizing is not retelling every event. It is condensing the information down to only the most important facts.

Using the vocabulary words from the Heads Up activity or other words from the folktale that you think are appropriate, identify ten key words that would best describe the folktale. Write them in the spaces below. The ten words do not need to go together to form a sentence.

My Key Words

_____

_____

_____

_____

_____

_____

_____

_____

_____

_____

Write to Learn In the Heads Up section you made a prediction, summarizing the folktale before you read. Now based on the ten words you identified on page 43 and your reading of the story, write a three-sentence summary of the story. Remember, summarizing is not retelling the whole story; it is reviewing the most important events.

Lesson 5

The Mighty Power Plus Game

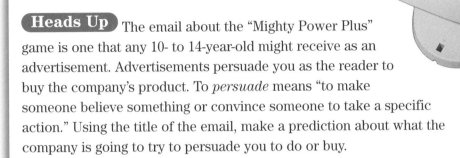

• *Email Advertisement*

Heads Up The email about the "Mighty Power Plus" game is one that any 10- to 14-year-old might receive as an advertisement. Advertisements persuade you as the reader to buy the company's product. To *persuade* means "to make someone believe something or convince someone to take a specific action." Using the title of the email, make a prediction about what the company is going to try to persuade you to do or buy.

My Prediction

_____

_____

_____

_____

_____

_____

_____

continued

If the intent of an advertisement is to persuade the reader to buy the product, why would word choice be so critical? Think about the title, "The Mighty Power Plus Game." Why might the company choose words such as *mighty*, *power*, and *plus*? Write your thoughts below.

My Thoughts

_____

_____

_____

_____

_____

_____

_____

As you read, be an active reader by recording your thoughts beside each Think-Along Question. Also, as you read, circle or highlight any words you don't know.

The Mighty Power Plus Game

by Jan Keese

1   **Date:** December 23, 2002
    To: 10-to14-year-oldbuyer@sendusmoney.net

> Why do you think the company would identify a specific age group?

    From: mpp@perfectiongames.com
    Subject: Don't miss this opportunity!

> Predict what you think the email is going to say.

2   Don't be the last one on your block to own the new "Mighty Power Plus" computer game. You've played the original for years, but now it's time to step up to the next generation of computer games. Don't be a "has been"; be a leader!

> Why do you think the company chose the word *leader* in this paragraph?

3   For a limited time only, you can pick up your copy of "Mighty Power Plus" for a greatly reduced price. This reduced price is a **fraction** of the cost of the game once this offer **expires**. Buying now means saving now!

> Can you think of a time when you wanted to buy something because it was on sale? What was it? Did you buy it?

4   With better graphics; **higher** levels; and new, fierce competitors, it will prove to be a game of the future. This is a game you don't want to miss!

5   This offer won't last long, so act now and be a winner!

> How does a winner act or feel?

Make Sense of Words Most words have multiple meanings. So, in order to determine their meanings, the words need to be read in the context of the story. Sometimes the multiple meanings are closely related with only slight variations. Complete the chart below for three words from the "Mighty Power Plus" email advertisement.

Word	Meaning in story	A new sentence showing another meaning
fraction (¶3)		
expires (¶3)		
higher (¶4)		

Now look back at the other words you marked in the text. Can you use this vocabulary strategy to help you figure out the meanings of those words?

Read with Understanding The intent of the email advertisement is to encourage the reader to purchase the "Mighty Power Plus" game. According to the email, which statement is true?

① The old game will no longer work.

② You can only purchase this new game for one day.

③ You don't need much money to buy this new game.

④ If you want to be a winner, you will purchase this game.

Understand by Seeing It The company behind the "Mighty Power Plus" computer game used many strategies to entice the reader to purchase it. That is what advertisers do. They think of what they can say or show so that the consumer will want to buy the product. Fill in the web below with words or phrases the company used to make the consumer, or reader, want to buy the computer game.

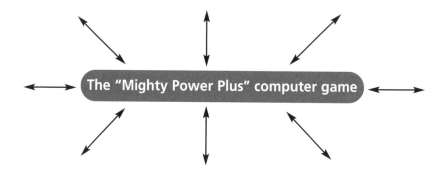

Which two words or phrases from your completed web do you think would have the most appeal to a 10- to 14-year-old? Write them below.

_____

_____

Write to Learn   Often an advertisement has a graphic or picture that supports what the text says. Create a graphic to support this advertisement, and then write a caption to go with it.

My Ad Graphic

Caption _____

Lesson 6

Letter to Attorney General Francis Biddle

• *Letter*

Heads Up Iwao Matsushita's letter to Attorney General Francis Biddle is an example of persuasive writing. Persuasive writing is used to either convince the reader to accept a belief, position, or opinion or to take a specific action.

Look at the Before Reading column below. Circle whether you agree or disagree with each statement. After you finish reading the letter, go back to the After Reading column and decide whether you agree or disagree with each statement. Did you change any of your answers?

Anticipation Guide

Before Reading	Statement	After Reading
Agree *Disagree*	1. The U.S. government has forced innocent citizens to live in camps because of their ethnic background.	*Agree* *Disagree*
Agree *Disagree*	2. The United States and Japan were allies during World War II.	*Agree* *Disagree*
Agree *Disagree*	3. The U.S. government never admits to making mistakes.	*Agree* *Disagree*
Agree *Disagree*	4. People who aren't born in this country can still be loyal citizens.	*Agree* *Disagree*
Agree *Disagree*	5. Government officials never respond to letters from citizens.	*Agree* *Disagree*

The Think-Along Questions interjected throughout the text will help focus your thinking, especially about persuasive writing. Also, as you read, circle or highlight any words you don't know.

Letter to Attorney General Francis Biddle

by Iwao Matsushita

On February 19, 1942, President Franklin D. Roosevelt signed Executive Order 9066. This directed the U.S. government to put 120,000 Japanese Americans, including U.S. citizens, in relocation centers in ten states. Although initially the U.S. government claimed it was trying to protect Japanese Americans, it later admitted that what it did was cruel and wrong. In August 1988, the U.S. government passed a law giving every living Japanese American who had been forced into a relocation center $20,000 and an official apology.

Fort Missoula, Montana
Jan. 2, 1943

The Honorable Francis Biddle,
Attorney General,
Washington, D.C.

Dear Mr. Biddle,

1   I, Iwao Matsushita, an alien Japanese, have been detained in Fort Missoula since Dec. 28, 1941, and I was recently notified about my internment order, despite the fact the Hearing Board made a recommendation for my release.

> **Why do you think Iwao was interned despite the Hearing Board's recommendation?**

2   Since I read your article in a magazine last spring, regarding your policy of treating "alien enemies"—the words, you mentioned, you even didn't like to use—you have been occupying the innermost shrine of my heart as my only refuge and savior. So when I received your internment order, I was naturally greatly disappointed, because according to your interpretation in the magazine, you intern only those aliens whom you consider to be potentially dangerous to the public safety.

3   Now, my conscience urges me to make a personal heart-to-heart appeal to you. Kindly allow me to make a brief statement about myself.

> **What about the tone of the letter so far makes it persuasive?**

continued

Letter to Attorney General Francis Biddle continued

4   I was born a Christian in a Methodist minister's family, educated in an American Mission School, came to this country in 1919 from sheer admiration of the American way of life. I have always been living, almost half and the best part of my life, in Seattle, Wash., and never went to Japan for the last twenty-four years, despite the fact there were many such opportunities, simply because I liked this country, and the principles on which it stands.

5   I have never broken any Federal, State, Municipal, or even traffic laws, and paid taxes regularly. I believe myself one of the most upright persons. I have never been, am not, and will never be potentially dangerous to the safety of the United States. There isn't an iota of dangerous elements in me, nor should there be any such evidence against me.

6   On the contrary I have done much good to the American public. For instance, several years ago, I taught Japanese Language in the University of Washington, Seattle, without any compensation to help out the institution, which couldn't get appropriation for that purpose from the State. I might prove to be of some service in this capacity.

Why do you think he taught Japanese without pay?

7   I am quite sure that my life history and my statement regarding loyalty in the hearing record will certainly convince you that I am a bona fide loyal resident.

8   My wife, with whom I have never been separated even for a short time during the last twenty-five years, and who has the same loyalty and admiration for this country, is living helplessly and sorrowfully in Idaho Relocation Center. You are the only person who can make us join in happiness and let us continue to enjoy the American life.

Have you ever been separated from your family or close friends for a significant amount of time? How did you feel?

9   Therefore, please give my case your special reconsideration and let me anticipate your favorable answer.

Yours respectfully,
Iwao Matsushita

Predict what will happen to Iwao Matsushita.

A year later, Matsushita and his wife were reunited in Iowa.

Make Sense of Words Sometimes words carry meaning beyond their literal definitions. *Connotation* is the associations, feelings, or images carried by a word. Explore *connotation* by applying it to the word *mother*.

What is the literal definition of *mother*?

_____

Now, what associations, feelings, or images are carried by the word *mother*?

_____

_____

_____

This letter uses the word **alien**. Iwao Matsushita even writes to Francis Biddle, "Since I read your article in a magazine last spring, regarding your policy of treating '**alien** enemies'—the words, you mentioned, you even didn't like to use . . ." What reason would Francis Biddle have for not wanting to use the word **alien**, along with enemy? What *connotations* does **alien** have?

First, write your first impression of **alien**. What comes to mind when you first hear the word? Write or draw your first thought.

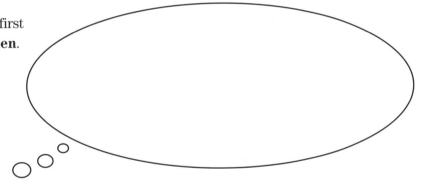

Now, look up the word **alien** in the dictionary. What meaning does it have as it relates to the letter you just read?

_____

Finally, what *connotations* does **alien** have? Are they good or bad? Is **alien** seen as a positive word or a negative word? Write the *connotations* of **alien** below.

_____

_____

_____

Read with Understanding Iwao Matsushita's letter was written for the purpose of persuading Attorney General Francis Biddle to reconsider his and his wife's internment orders. What do you think is the most likely reason his persuasive letter was effective?

① Attorney General Biddle was afraid Matsushita would go back to live in Japan.

② Matsushita was respectful and provided valid points about why he wasn't a threat.

③ Matsushita threatened to never pay taxes again.

④ Attorney General Biddle was a graduate of the University of Washington, Seattle.

WARTIME CIVIL CONTROL ADMINISTRATION
~~SE~~ COMMAND AND FOURTH ARMY
Presidio of San Francisco, California
April 1, 1942

INSTRUCTIONS
TO ALL PERSONS OF
JAPANESE
ANCESTRY
Living in the Following Area:

All that portion of the City and County of San Francisco, State of California, lying generally west of the north-south line established by Junipero Serra Boulevard, Worchester Avenue, and Nineteenth Avenue, and lying generally north of the east-west line established by California Street, to the intersection of Market Street, and thence on Market Street to San Francisco Bay.

All Japanese persons, both alien and non-alien, will be evacuated from the above designated area by 12:00 o'clock noon Tuesday, April 7, 1942.

No Japanese person will be permitted to enter or leave the above described area after 8:00 a.m., Thursday, April 2, 1942, without obtaining special permission from the Provost Marshal at the Civil Control Station located at:

1701 Van Ness Avenue
San Francisco, California

The Civil Control Station is equipped to assist the Japanese population affected by this evacuation in the following ways:

1. Give advice and instructions on the evacuation.
2. Provide services with respect to the ~~man~~

Understand by Seeing It The power of persuasion is in the effect it has on the receiver. This effect plays on the emotions of the reader. Typical types of emotional appeals include:

Companionship—reader's desire to be with another person or other people

Curiosity—reader's desire to answer the why, when, where, who, what, and how

Destruction—reader's desire to overthrow a rule, institution, problem, etc.

Guilt—reader's desire not to feel inadequate or guilty about the situation

Independence—reader's desire to make own decision

Loyalty—reader's desire to show support for cause/product

Power and Authority—reader's desire to feel strong and in control

Sympathy—reader's tendency to feel sorry for others/objects/situations

Identify three words or phrases from the letter that Iwao Matsushita uses to appeal to Attorney General Biddle and to persuade him to reconsider his internment order. Then identify the type of emotional appeal and why it might be effective. An example has been done for you.

Word or phrase from letter	Type of emotional appeal	Why might this be effective?
" 'alien enemies'—the words, you mentioned, you even didn't like to use"	Guilt	Attorney General Biddle might feel guilty about detaining a man who was clearly not an "enemy"

Write to Learn Now that you have seen evidence that writing to persuade can be effective and have positive results, write an email to your teacher trying to persuade him or her not to give you any homework tonight. Remember, the email doesn't have to be lengthy if what it says is powerful!

Send

To:
From:
Subject:

All Together Now

• Speech

Heads Up At the Democratic National Convention in 1992, Barbara Jordan spoke, offering suggestions for promoting tolerance and equality in America. Jordan was the first African American woman from the South to serve in the U.S. Congress. As you read this speech, you need to be thinking about the reading strategies you have worked on throughout the previous lessons. These strategies include *finding relevant details*, *summarizing*, and *recognizing persuasive techniques*. All three strategies can be used to help you understand the message of the speech.

Scan the speech. Find ten words that you predict will be important in the speech. Record them below.

Important Words

_____ _____

_____ _____

_____ _____

_____ _____

_____ _____

continued

Now, based on these ten words, predict what you think the speech will be about.

My Prediction

_____

_____

_____

_____

_____

_____

As a strategic reader, you will ask yourself questions as you read. Sometimes you will predict what's coming next. Other times you will make connections between what you're reading and your own life. And sometimes you are just confused and will ask yourself questions to clarify what you are reading.

The Think-Along Questions in this review lesson will not be as specific as the Think-Along Questions in the previous lessons. They will guide you to be more independent in thinking about what you are reading. Record your thoughts beside each question.

All Together Now

by Barbara Jordan

My Thoughts

1   When I look at race relations today I can see that some positive changes have come about. But much remains to be done, and the answer does not lie in more legislation. We have the legislation we need; we have the laws. Frankly, I don't believe that the task of bringing us all together can be accomplished by government. What we need now is soul force—the efforts of people working on a small scale to build a truly **tolerant**, harmonious society. And parents can do a great deal to create that tolerant society.

> What are you thinking? What questions do you have?

2   We all know that race relations in America have had a very rocky history. Think about the 1960s when Dr. Martin Luther King Jr. was in his heyday and there were marches and protests against segregation and discrimination. The movement culminated in 1963 with the March on Washington.

3   Following that event, race relations reached an all-time peak. President Lyndon B. Johnson pushed through the Civil Rights Act of 1964, which remains the fundamental piece of civil rights legislation in this century. The Voting Rights Act of 1965 ensured that everyone in our country could vote. At last, black people and white people seemed ready to live together in peace.

4   But that is not what happened. By the 1990s the good feelings had diminished. Today the nation seems to be suffering from compassion fatigue, and issues such as race relations and civil rights have never regained momentum.

> What are you thinking here? Do you understand what you are reading? What questions do you have?

5   Those issues, however, remain crucial. As our society becomes more diverse, people of all races and backgrounds will have to learn to live together. If we don't think this is important, all we have to do is look at the situation in Bosnia today.

continued

All Together Now continued

6   How do we create a harmonious society out of so many kinds of people? The key is tolerance—the one value that is indispensable in creating community.

What are you thinking now? Are you understanding all of the vocabulary words? What questions do you have?

7   If we are concerned about community, if it is important to us that people not feel excluded, then we have to do something. Each of us can decide to have one friend of a different race or background in our mix of friends. If we do this, we'll be working together to push things forward.

8   One thing is clear to me: We, as human beings, must be willing to accept people who are different from ourselves. I must be willing to accept people who don't look as I do and don't talk as I do. It is crucial that I am open to their feelings, their inner reality.

9   What can parents do? We can put our faith in young people as a positive force. I have yet to find a racist baby. Babies come into the world as blank slates and, with their beautiful innocence, see others not as different but as enjoyable companions. Children learn ideas and attitudes from the adults who nurture them. I absolutely believe that children do not adopt prejudices unless they absorb them from their parents or teachers.

Do you agree or disagree with this? Why?

10   The best way to get this country faithful to the American dream of tolerance and equality is to start small. Parents can actively encourage their children to be in the company of people who are of other racial and ethnic backgrounds. If a child thinks, "Well, that person's color is not the same as mine, but she must be okay because she likes to play with the same things I like to play with," that child will grow up with a broader sense of humanity.

11   I'm an incurable optimist. For the rest of the time that I have left on this planet I want to bring people together. You might think of this as a labor of love. Now, I know that love means different things to different people. But what I mean is this: I care about you because you are a fellow human being and I find it okay in my mind, in my heart, to simply say to you, I love you. And maybe that would encourage you to love me in return.

12   It is possible for all of us to work on this—at home, in our schools, at our jobs. It is possible to work on human relationships in every area of our lives.

What are your thoughts as you finish reading this speech?

My Thoughts

Read with Understanding Think about Barbara Jordan's speech as you answer the following questions.

1. Which statement is most likely true about Barbara Jordan?
   Ⓐ She has likely felt discriminated against at some point in her life.
   Ⓑ She has four children of her own.
   Ⓒ She has given many important speeches in her life.
   Ⓓ She only cares about African Americans.

2. The definition that most closely defines **tolerant** as used in this speech is
   Ⓐ "being kind."
   Ⓑ "accepting all people."
   Ⓒ "having African American friends."
   Ⓓ "donating money to charities."

3. To whom does Barbara Jordan appeal in her speech?
   Ⓐ lawmakers to make better laws
   Ⓑ President Lyndon Johnson to insist people do the right thing
   Ⓒ all people to take responsibility for the treatment of others
   Ⓓ African Americans to be more likeable

4. Which conclusion about Barbara Jordan could you make?
   Ⓐ She is compassionate.
   Ⓑ She is famous.
   Ⓒ History was her favorite subject in school.
   Ⓓ She likes to give speeches.

5. Which detail best supports the main idea of this speech?
   Ⓐ "Race relations" refers to just African Americans.
   Ⓑ Parents can encourage their children to have friends from different racial backgrounds.
   Ⓒ We need to change legislation about race relations.
   Ⓓ The Civil Rights Act was passed in 1964.

Understand by Seeing It   Think about all the information that Barbara Jordan shared in her speech. You know that to *summarize* means to identify the important information and organize it in a format to share. Write the topic of the speech in the center oval below. Write three important relevant details around the oval.

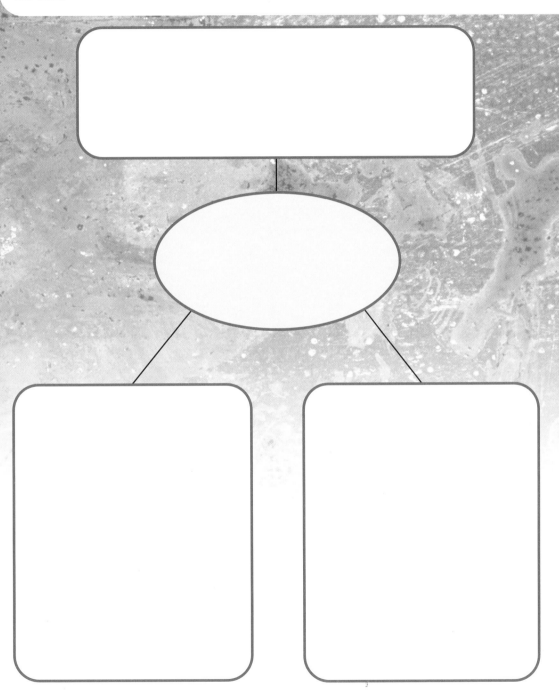

Write to Learn Now based on the important relevant details that you have identified, write a two-sentence summary of the speech.

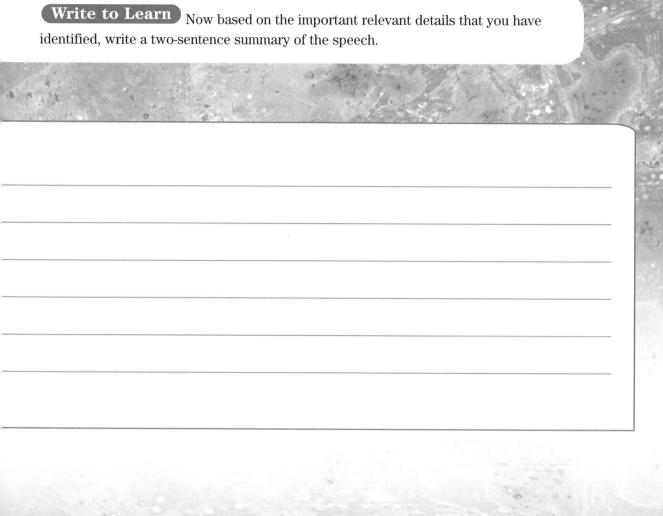

The Fastest Runner

• Short Story

Listening comprehension is a valuable skill. Learning and practicing good listening skills will be helpful to you in your life inside and outside of school. When you listen, it is important to sit quietly and focus your attention on the speaker.

Listen as your teacher reads the story "The Fastest Runner." Your teacher will stop about halfway through and ask you to make a prediction by answering the first question below.

1. Who do you think the fastest runner is?

_____

After your teacher finishes reading "The Fastest Runner," answer the second question below.

2. What was the surprise in the story?

_____

_____

Now your teacher will read "The Fastest Runner" again. Listen carefully and answer the question below.

3. What clues did the author give you about the fastest runner's identity?

Section 2

Lesson 7

This Way Nobody Gets the Blame

• *Short Story*

Heads Up Think about when you read a story. Does the author tell you everything you need to know, or do you have to figure out some information on your own? As a strategic reader, you take what you already know with you when you read. This helps you fill in the gaps authors leave. When you fill in the gaps, you are *making inferences*.

You are about to read a short story mystery called "This Way Nobody Gets the Blame." Take a look at the title. What might you infer the story to be about, keeping in mind that it is a short story and there is a hint of mystery involved? Write a plot "summary" of your prediction by filling in the graphic organizer on the next page.

continued

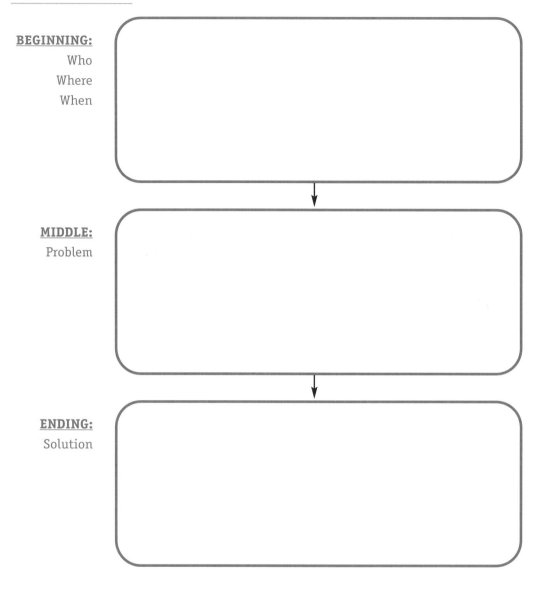

BEGINNING:
Who
Where
When

MIDDLE:
Problem

ENDING:
Solution

Making inferences is connecting what is written to your experiences and coming up with an "informed guess."

Use the Think-Along Questions and your knowledge of mysteries to infer what is happening and why it is happening as you read the short story. Record your thoughts beside each question. Also, as you read, circle or highlight any words you don't know.

This Way Nobody Gets the Blame

by Lesley Grant-Adamson

1   This way," he said, "nobody gets the blame."

Predict the event for which no one is getting the blame.

2   Ella gave him a teasing look, which he missed because he was striding along, quite quickly considering how much he had to carry. But he'd sounded so proud she couldn't resist saying: "It was very clever of you to work it all out, Phil."

3   He took the remark seriously. "You too, Ella. It's just as much your plan as mine."

4   "Well, whoever it belongs to, let's hope it works."

5   This time he stopped and looked hard at her. "You haven't spotted a flaw? I mean, if there's anything not quite right now's the time to . . ."

6   "No, no, it's perfect."

7   "You're sure?"

8   "Honestly. It's **foolproof**."

9   "And it's as good as done." He began to walk again, his waterproof jacket rustling.

10   The path narrowed and Ella trailed behind. Over to the right the sea heaved against a rocky shore. For the rest there was an empty hinterland, with sunlight fading on granite walls enclosing salty fields.

11   Philip urged her on with an impatient toss of his head, but she thought it added a touch of normality if she were dawdling, so she didn't hurry.

12   "Come on." He took up a studied, relaxed stance while waiting for her. He was a terribly unconvincing actor, his irritation undisguised. She'd experienced a lot of it lately. Nobody would have dreamed the whole mess was his fault and not hers.

What can you infer about Ella and Philip's relationship?

continued

This Way Nobody Gets the Blame continued

13   "*I am the innocent victim,*" she thought, dreamily, as she watched the waves rushing to destruction.

Have you ever felt you were wrongly blamed for something?

14   She turned the dreamy look into a smile as she drew nearer to her husband. "I'm trying to look natural, Phil. We shouldn't dash as though we expect every wave to be the last."

15   "I don't remember rehearsing this dithering when we did our trial runs."

16   She winced at the unfortunate word, trial, but Philip appeared not to notice and strode on. After a few paces he ushered her past him so that from then on he was following her, or rather he was shepherding her down the path.

17   They passed the kink where a big stone had broken free and the surface was slippery. Ella skipped swiftly on but she heard her husband's boots slide on the scree. He was fond of those boots, he'd had them for years, but there'd been too many slips for her to believe they gripped well.

18   Philip hadn't proved surefooted in other, figurative, ways either. He'd made a mess of his business and a worse one in borrowing to wriggle out of trouble. And then he'd done the very silly thing.

What questions might you have for Philip about the mess he's made?

19   Like everything else about him, his mistake, his crime, was unoriginal. It used to be called borrowing from Peter to pay Paul, but now there were bleaker ways of describing it. Misappropriation, fraud, or embezzlement.

What do *misappropriation, fraud,* and *embezzlement* mean?

They came to the same thing: he'd stolen money.

20   "We're in a fix," he'd admitted to Ella the day he told her about the huge debt, the investor who'd be plundered, and the sham their lives had become.

21   "You mean we'll have to sell Silver Acre?"

22   She loved the old house, its cozy position in a hollow overlooking the sea, and the status that being its owner conferred on her. She'd never been comfortable before. Her childhood had been poor, and in the years when Philip was

building his business they'd scraped by in a bungalow on a modern estate. At Silver Acre she felt truly at home for the first time in her life.

23 When he didn't answer her question, she'd asked another one: "Who else knows about this?"

24 "Nobody."

25 "Not even Heidi?"

26 "Not even her."

27 Heidi was his assistant, an Austrian woman with bright blue eyes and a singsong accent. At one time Ella suspected she was rather closer to him than that, but Philip had persuaded her not.

28 "Is there nothing else we can do?"

29 He gave a bitter laugh. "Not to save the house. We offered it as security and the bank will take it."

30 "Are we going bankrupt?"

31 He spoke flatly, as though explaining to someone especially dim. "*We're* going to be bankrupt and *I'm* probably going to be in prison."

32 "But . . ."

33 "But what? Don't you think I've thought all around this, before I decided I had to tell you?"

> Why would Philip have only told his wife as a last resort?

34 "Yes, I'm sure you did."

35 It had always been his way to do things and tell her afterwards. She used to protest at him shutting her out but it made no difference because it was his nature.

36 For a second she was so angry with him that she didn't care whether he went to prison or not. It would be what he deserved for wrecking her life as well as his own, she thought; but the thought was very brief. "There must be a way," she said.

37 And she saw from his face that he thought so, too. Before long they were plotting.

continued

Unit 4: Make Inferences |

38   The path turned into rugged steps. Ella climbed down easily. On the first visit she'd found it tricky but they'd tramped this route half a dozen times since that evening of plotting. If anyone had cared to look they would have noticed that the couple from Silver Acre liked to go fishing below the cliffs some evenings.

39   But no one would have guessed that one evening their car was to be abandoned where they usually parked it, near the start of the path. Or that a van had been bought especially for them to flee in and lay hidden in a barn on the edge of their land. Or that in its glove box were false passports. Or that Philip had rounded up what was left of the money, a substantial amount as long as no debts were honored, and had transferred it abroad.

40   Where the steps met the rocks Ella paused once again and gazed around. A wave frothed towards her. The lower step was awash, her boots and ankles drenched.

> Predict what they are planning to do.

41   Behind her Philip said: "You see? If you hadn't been hanging about we'd have been over without getting wet."

42   He splashed past her and hoisted himself up on to the rocks. "Come on," he shouted back. "Give me a hand with this."

43   Ella leaped across while the water was receding, perched on her usual toehold and reached the top of the rock. A buffeting wind was coming from the west. Waves were jagged white lines when they were far out, but whisked into fury near the shore. With a terrible sucking, the water snatched what it could from the land.

44   While Philip battled to position their rods, she stayed where she was. They'd hoped for a lively sea, to give credence to the idea that they'd been swept away and drowned. So far, luck was with them.

45   She couldn't just stand there, watching him. He seemed to be having trouble with her rod, and he gestured for her to help. For a moment she was rooted. Then she darted forward, keen to get it done.

46   Ella sprang at him and sent him over the edge. He had no chance, in those slippery boots of his. She didn't hear him cry out, but she saw his astonishment. In the instant before she made contact, he'd been turning towards her, arm outstretched. Her first thought, as he disappeared into the spray, was that she was fortunate to have avoided his clutching hand. If he'd moved more quickly, or if she'd been slower, he would certainly have got a grip on her sleeve and she could have plunged into the sea.

> Is there any reason to believe Philip wasn't really having trouble with the rod? Why or why not?

47   Alone, she followed the escape route along the cliff tip. Rain was blowing on the wind and the light was as poor as she hoped. Any lighter and she might be recognized, and darker and she'd need a torch. Soon the waves were turbulent ghosts on a black sea. She cut inland.

48   At last she drew close to the barn. Its door was rattling in the wind. "*Philip ought to have made it secure,*" she thought crossly. "*Supposing it had blown open and someone had noticed the van?*"

49   Inside the barn it was totally dark. She felt the van's bumper against her leg and squeezed round to the driver's door. As she opened it, everything collapsed in a whirl of confusion.

50   A woman in the passenger seat was gabbling at her in a singsong voice, pawing at her, "Oh, Philip, I thought you'd never come! How did it go? Did she suspect anything? It must have been absolutely terrible for you . . ."

Make Sense of Words As a strategic reader, you are an active learner of vocabulary rather than a passive learner. This means that when you read, you think about a key vocabulary word and discover what it means and how it can be used. You can be an active learner of vocabulary in a variety of ways. One active learning strategy is going beyond the definition by identifying characteristics and applying them to what you know.

Complete the following graphic organizer for the word **foolproof** found in paragraph 8.

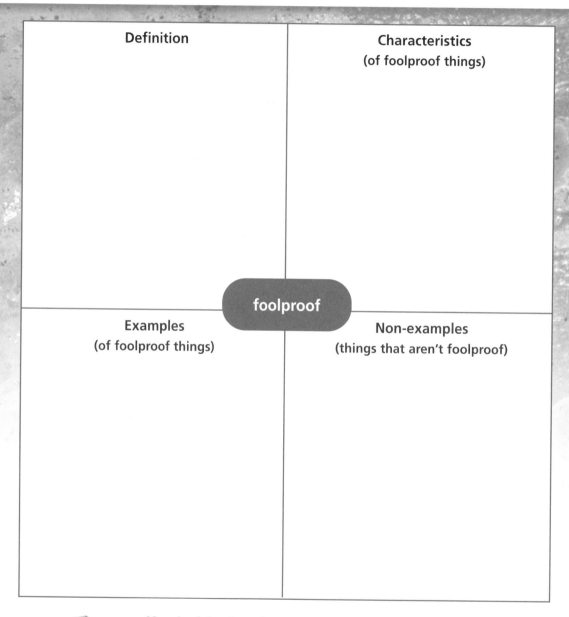

Definition	Characteristics (of foolproof things)

foolproof

Examples (of foolproof things)	Non-examples (things that aren't foolproof)

Now look back at the other words you marked in the text. Can you use this vocabulary strategy to help you figure out the meanings of those words?

Read with Understanding Think about how the story ended. Which statement below best represents your final *inference* regarding the foolproof plan?

① Ella planned to drown Philip and run away with her best friend.

② Philip intended to commit suicide so that he wouldn't be sent to prison.

③ Ella and Philip decided against fishing because the sea was so rough.

④ Philip planned to drown Ella and run off with the woman waiting in the van.

Understand by Seeing It Mystery is designed to keep the reader wondering and questioning what is going to happen next, why something is as it is, or what the real meaning is. Look back at the short story and think about *inferences* you made and the words and phrases that led you to make them. Fill in the chart below.

Inferences	Words or phrases from the story

Write to Learn Based on your *inferences*, write a conclusion to the story.

Lesson 8

I've Got Your Number

• *Editorial*

Heads Up What associations do you make with the word *discrimination*? Fill in the web below with words or phrases that you associate with *discrimination*. Use the nonshaded ovals to record subcategories that you associate with this word. An example might be "gender." Then record associations you have with your subcategory words or phrases in the shaded ovals.

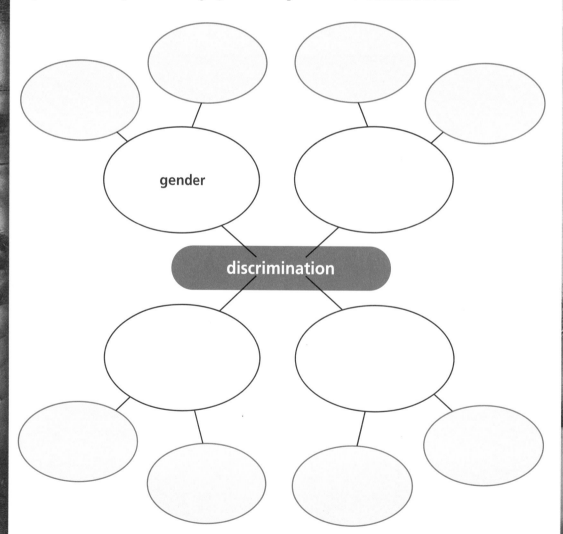

An editorial is intended to communicate the writer's opinion to the public. As you read "I've Got Your Number," you will *infer* the author's opinion and purpose for writing this editorial. When you infer, you take what you know about a topic and merge it with what you read to gain a new understanding. An *inference* is based on the text itself and your background experiences.

Use the Think-Along Questions to help focus your thinking as you read. Record your thoughts beside each question. Also, as you read, circle or highlight any words you don't know.

I've Got Your Number
by Robe Imbriano

> Predict what number the author is referring to.

1   Last Sunday night, sometime after 10:30 p.m., I put an end to my seventh straight day of work. I left behind the stress of my office to confront another set of pressures—finding transportation home on the coldest day of the year.

2   I didn't have the right change for a bus, nor had I any tokens. So when I found both booths at the 66th Street subway station closed, I reemerged to ground level— flustered, a shade more than tired and a hair less than frostbitten—and began to search for a yellow cab with a light on top.

> What can you infer about the author so far?

3   That's where we met.

4   Remember me?

5   I was the fairly well-dressed man on the corner of 66th Street and Broadway, facing uptown. Surely you must; I was the only one there. I was waving to you as I'd imagine a refugee in a war-torn country would wave to his would-be savior.

> Why would he refer to the cab driver as his "would-be savior"?

6   Any **recollection**?

7   You slowed, your cab clearly empty, its back seat filled only with warmth. You looked at me—turned your head in my direction. Was that a smile that played on your lips?

8   Just as people on foot nod their heads in recognition at those they find vaguely familiar, cabbies, too, signal pedestrian acquaintances, particularly those of my stripe.

> Infer what the author means by "those of my stripe."

9   You accelerated.

10 Now, you weren't off duty. If perhaps I had been mistaken, my doubts were soon resolved when, at the next block, you stopped for the fairly well-dressed man at the corner of 67th Street and Broadway.

What questions might you ask the cab driver?

11 The white man at the corner of 67th Street and Broadway.

12 Through the tears that the subzero wind brought to and blew from my eyes, I saw two more of your colleagues pass underneath my raised arm.

13 My raised black arm.

14 Until we meet again, Mr. T57030T.

15 Until we meet again.

Describe a time when you felt you were discriminated against or treated unfairly.

My Thoughts

Make Sense of Words Often to fully understand a vocabulary word and its intended meaning, you need to look for parts of the word as well as the base word. Prefixes and suffixes are added to slightly change the meaning of a base word. A prefix is added to the beginning of a base word, and a suffix is added to the end.

Complete the word tree for **recollection**, found in paragraph 6.

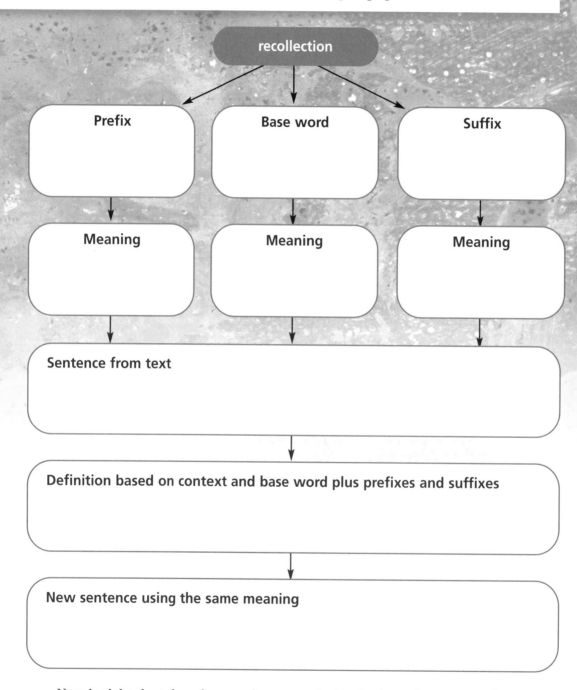

recollection

| Prefix | Base word | Suffix |

| Meaning | Meaning | Meaning |

Sentence from text

Definition based on context and base word plus prefixes and suffixes

New sentence using the same meaning

Now look back at the other words you marked in the text. Can you use this vocabulary strategy to help you figure out the meanings of those words?

Read with Understanding The writer of the editorial never states directly why he thinks the cab driver did not stop. Obviously, you as the reader will never know for sure what was going on inside the driver's head, but based on what you read and what you *inferred*, what explanation might you give for why the cab driver didn't stop?

① He was running out of gas.

② He thought the other person would give a bigger tip.

③ He didn't see Robe Imbriano.

④ He was prejudiced against a person with dark skin.

Understand by Seeing It You can draw *inferences* about characters as well as about plot, events, and conclusions. Complete the two graphic organizers below about Robe Imbriano and the cab driver.

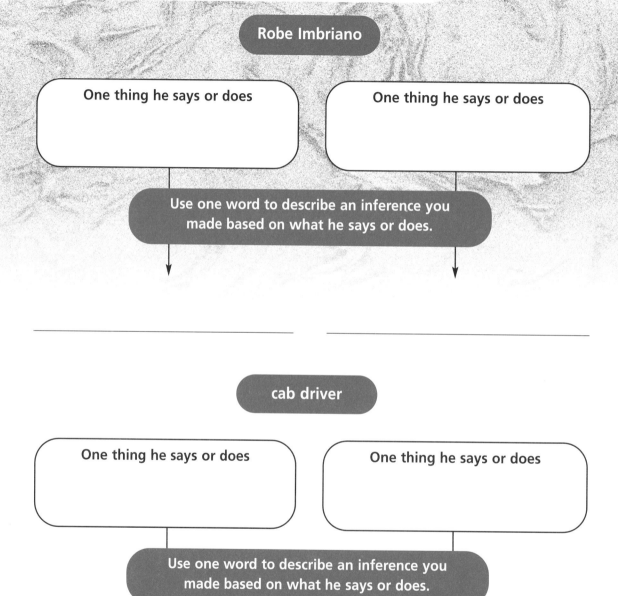

Robe Imbriano

One thing he says or does

One thing he says or does

Use one word to describe an inference you made based on what he says or does.

cab driver

One thing he says or does

One thing he says or does

Use one word to describe an inference you made based on what he says or does.

Write to Learn Based on what you have *inferred*, what do you think the cab driver would do if he read this editorial in the newspaper? Write a monologue of the cab driver's thoughts while and after reading it.

Lesson 9

This Girl Gets Her Kicks

• *Article*

Heads Up What comes to mind when you read the phrase "female football player"? Maybe you think "uncommon" or "muscular." Maybe you know a girl who plays football. Write all of your associations on the lines of the web below. Try to fill in every line.

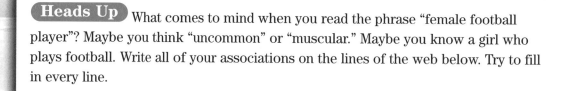

Female football player

Choose two of your associations from the previous page. Reflect on why you wrote each of them.

Association: _____

Why you think you wrote it: _____

_____

Association: _____

Why you think you wrote it: _____

_____

As you read "This Girl Gets Her Kicks," notice how the author describes the main character of the essay. An author provides *characterization* through:

- direct description
- what the character does
- what the character says
- what the character thinks
- what other people say about the character
- how other people react to the character

Decide if you *characterized* a female football player the same way the author did.

The Think-Along Questions will help you focus on characterization while also practicing other strategies that make you an active reader. Record your thoughts beside each question. Also, as you read, circle or highlight any words you don't know.

This Girl Gets Her Kicks

by Rick Reilly

1   Q: *How come nobody said a word last week after the Chatfield (Colo.) High homecoming queen accepted a single white rose at halftime of the football game, locked arms with the king and then ripped off her satin sash and sprinted into the players' locker room?*

A: *She still had two quarters to play.*

2   Katie Hnida (pronounced NYE-duh) is 17, with long blond hair, melt-your-heart blue eyes, and legs that won't quit kicking. This season she's perfect: 23 for 23 on extra points, 3 for 3 on field goals and 1 for 1 in homecoming queen elections.

> After reading the first two paragraphs, what other characteristics do you predict Katie will have?

3   Among the best sports moments of the 1990s, this one has to be in the top 10: Katie tearing off her helmet at the end of the first half, taking her place among other members of the homecoming court in their dresses and high heels, being announced as queen, wriggling the sash on over her shoulder pads, waving thanks to everybody, smiling for the photographers and sprinting to the dressing room. "I only had a minute," she says of her **coronation**.

4   Is this a great time or what? We're past the 1970s, when girls had two options in sports: cheerleader or pep squad. We're past the '80s, when girls had two options in life: to be a jock or a girl.

> How is it in your school? Can a girl be both a jock and a girl?

Now we're into the Katie Era when a young lady can kick the winning field goal on Saturday afternoon and look drop-dead in her spaghetti-strap number on Saturday night. "I know I looked gross at halftime," Katie says. "No makeup or anything. But I'm a football player. How else am I going to look?"

5   Actually, the only way anyone on the other team can guess that the 5' 9", 135-pound Katie is a girl is by the ponytail that runs out from beneath her helmet and down her back. One time, as a freshman, she got flattened after a PAT by a massive nosetackle, who ended up on top of her. They both opened their eyes at the same time, only it was the nosetackle who screamed, "You're a girl!"

6   Not that guys on the Chatfield High team seem to notice much. "I don't mind when they burp and spit around me," she says. "It lets me know they think of me as their teammate."

> How do you think Katie's teammates feel about having a girl on their team?

7   Another first: players thanked for impersonating water buffalo.

> What does the writer mean by this?

8   Katie's life can be strange. After one game last year the Chatfield players and their opponents were exchanging postgame handshakes when a hulk on the other team stopped Katie and asked, "Do you have another number besides 40 I could possibly have?" She didn't bite, but it still goes down as the single best pickup line in high school football history.

9   The only downside of the whole thing is that Katie has to shower and dress in the girls' locker room, away from the rest of the team. "Sometimes we'll win a big game and I can hear all the guys whooping it up," she says, "and I want to get in there with them."

> Knowing what you do about Katie at this point, why do you think she plays football?

10   Other than that, Katie "gets to be who she wants to be," says her mother, Anne, who never had that chance in high school. "I kept stats for the boys' basketball team," she says. Katie, meanwhile, has a 3.2 grade point average, writes and edits for the school newspaper, plays soccer in the spring, doesn't drink, won't smoke, can take a lick and kicks like a mule.

continued

My Thoughts

11   "Wearing a little skirt and jumping around after touchdowns isn't quite the same," she says. "I want the competition. I want to be part of the team. Girls ask me all the time, 'What's it like to be around all these gorgeous guys all the time?' They have no idea. I've seen these guys break down and cry in the huddle, and I've seen them so incredibly happy after a big win. I wouldn't trade anything for what I've had, being part of this team."

What question do you have for Katie?

12   Yeah, she'd even trade the sash. "Ten years from now, nobody's going to be impressed that I was homecoming queen," she says, "but they might think it was cool I could kick a 40-yard field goal."

13   Katie, who has already booted a 35-yarder, has this crazy dream that would make things even cooler. She wants to become the only Division I woman football player next season. Colorado coach Rick Neuheisel already has asked her to walk on. Me, I'd bet my last pair of hose on her.

14   One thing, no guy's ever going to have to give Katie his letter jacket. She's got her own, thanks. "I guess what I want to show is that it's O.K. to be athletic and feminine."

Do you agree or disagree with Katie? Why?

15   If nothing else, Katie Hnida gave us a rare moment, in which the homecoming queen walked off the field after the game and had little girls come up to her, saying, "Chin strap?"

Make Sense of Words When you come across an unknown word, you can sometimes figure out its meaning without looking it up in a dictionary or asking a teacher or friend. Sometimes the words and phrases near the unknown word provide enough clues. These are called *context clues*.

Go back to paragraph 3 of "This Girl Gets Her Kicks." Find the sentence, " 'I only had a minute,' she says of her **coronation**." **Coronation** is the featured vocabulary word in this lesson. Take a look at the words and phrases in that paragraph. Then fill in the graphic organizer below.

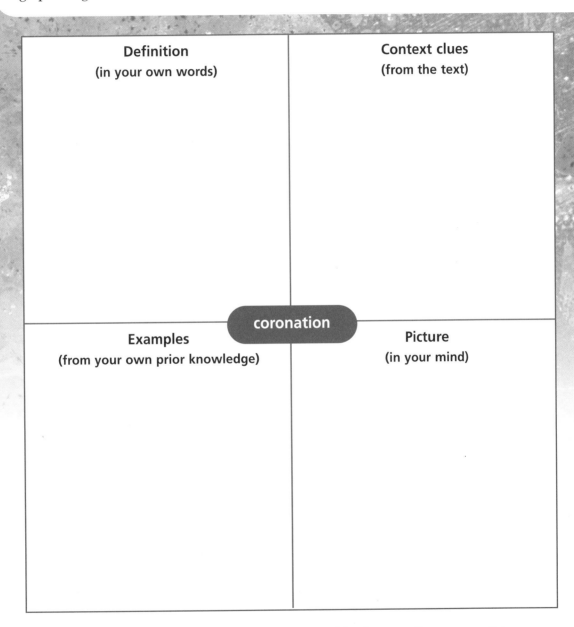

Definition (in your own words)	Context clues (from the text)

coronation

Examples (from your own prior knowledge)	Picture (in your mind)

Now look back at the other words you marked in the text. Can you use this vocabulary strategy to help you figure out the meanings of those words?

Read with Understanding Look back at the Heads Up section and review the different ways authors provide information about characters. How does the author, Rick Reilly, describe Katie Hnida in this sentence from "This Girl Gets Her Kicks"? Choose the best answer.

Colorado coach Rick Neuheisel already has asked Katie to walk on.

① direct description from the author

② how other people react to the character

③ what the character says

④ what the character does

Understand by Seeing It An author uses different techniques to bring a character to life. How did Rick Reilly describe Katie Hnida? Fill in the character map below, providing two examples for each *characterization* technique.

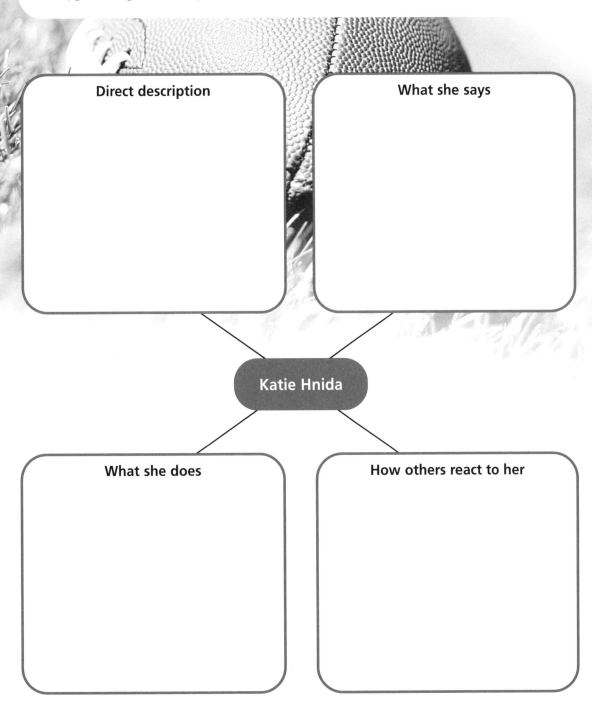

Direct description

What she says

Katie Hnida

What she does

How others react to her

Write to Learn Imagine that you are Katie Hnida. Based on what you know about her character, answer this college application question.

University of Colorado

Application for Admission

What was the most valuable lesson you learned in high school?

Lesson 10

Charles

• *Short Story*

Heads Up You will be reading a short story by Shirley Jackson called "Charles." This short story is about Laurie and his first few days of kindergarten. Think back to when you started kindergarten. Try to remember the experience and jot some notes in the boxes below.

What I thought	What I did

Think about your own experience as you compare it to the experience Laurie has as he starts kindergarten.

As you read, practice active reading strategies by responding to the Think-Along Questions throughout the text. Also, as you read, circle or highlight any words you don't know.

Charles

by Shirley Jackson

My Thoughts

1   The day my son Laurie started kindergarten he renounced corduroy overalls with bibs and began wearing blue jeans with a belt; I watched him go off the first morning with the older girl next door, seeing clearly that an era of my life was ended, my sweet-voiced nursery-school tot replaced by a long-trousered, swaggering character who forgot to stop at the corner and wave goodbye to me.

How do you think the mother felt when her son forgot to turn and wave goodbye on the very first day of school?

2   He came home the same way, the front door slamming open, his cap on the floor, and the voice suddenly became raucous shouting, "Isn't anybody *here*?"

3   At lunch he spoke insolently to his father, spilled his baby sister's milk, and remarked that his teacher said we were not to take the name of the Lord in vain.

4   "How *was* school today?" I asked, elaborately casual.

5   "All right," he said.

6   "Did you learn anything?" his father asked.

7   Laurie regarded his father coldly. "I didn't learn nothing," he said.

8   "Anything," I said. "Didn't learn anything."

9   "The teacher spanked a boy, though," Laurie said, addressing his bread and butter. "For being fresh," he added, with his mouth full.

10   "What did he do?" I asked. "Who was it?"

11   Laurie thought. "It was Charles," he said. "He was fresh. The teacher spanked him and made him stand in a corner. He was awfully fresh."

12   "What did he do?" I asked him again, but Laurie slid off his chair, took a cookie, and left, while his father was still saying, "See here, young man."

Predict what kind of parents Laurie has.

13   The next day Laurie remarked at lunch, as soon as he sat down, "Well, Charles was bad again today." He grinned enormously and said, "Today Charles hit the teacher."

14 "Good heavens," I said, mindful of the Lord's name, "I suppose he got spanked again?"

15 "He sure did," Laurie said. "Look up," he said to his father.

16 "What?" his father said, looking up.

17 "Look down," Laurie said. "Look at my thumb. Gee, you're dumb." He began to laugh insanely.

18 "Why did Charles hit the teacher?" I asked quickly.

19 "Because she tried to make him color with red crayons," Laurie said. "Charles wanted to color with green crayons so he hit the teacher and she spanked him and said nobody play with Charles but everybody did."

20 The third day—it was Wednesday of the first week— Charles bounced a seesaw onto the head of a little girl and made her bleed, and the teacher made him stay inside all during recess. Thursday Charles had to stand in a corner during story time because he kept pounding his feet on the floor. Friday Charles was deprived of blackboard privileges because he threw chalk.

> What would you do about Charles and kindergarten at this point if you were Laurie's parents?

21 On Saturday I remarked to my husband, "Do you think kindergarten is too unsettling for Laurie? All this toughness, and bad grammar, and this Charles boy sounds like such a bad influence."

22 "It'll be all right," my husband said reassuringly. "Bound to be people like Charles in the world. Might as well meet them now as later."

23 On Monday Laurie came home late, full of news. "Charles," he shouted as he came up the hill; I was waiting anxiously on the front steps. "Charles," Laurie yelled all the way up the hill, "Charles was bad again."

24 "Come right in," I said, as soon as he came close enough. "Lunch is waiting."

25 "You know what Charles did?" he demanded, following me through the door. "Charles yelled so in school they sent a boy in from first grade to tell the teacher she had to make Charles keep quiet, and so Charles had to stay after school. And so all the children stayed to watch him."

continued

Charles continued

26   "What did he do?" I asked.

27   "He just sat there," Laurie said, climbing into his chair at the table. "Hi, Pop, y'old dust mop."

28   "Charles had to stay after school today," I told my husband. "Everyone stayed with him."

29   "What does this Charles look like?" my husband asked Laurie. "What's his other name?"

30   "He's bigger than me," Laurie said. "And he doesn't have any rubbers and he doesn't ever wear a jacket."

31   Monday night was the first Parent-Teachers meeting, and only the fact that the baby had a cold kept me from going; I wanted passionately to meet Charles's mother. On Tuesday Laurie remarked suddenly, "Our teacher had a friend come to see her in school today."

What questions would you ask the teacher about Charles?

32   "Charles's mother?" my husband and I asked simultaneously.

33   "Naaah," Laurie said scornfully. "It was a man who came and made us do exercises, we had to touch our toes. Look." He climbed down from his chair and squatted down and touched his toes. "Like this," he said. He got solemnly back into his chair and said, picking up his fork, "Charles didn't even *do* exercises."

34   "That's fine," I said heartily. "Didn't Charles want to do exercises?"

35   "Naaah," Laurie said, "Charles was so fresh to the teacher's friend he wasn't *let* do exercises."

36   "Fresh again?" I said.

37   "He kicked the teacher's friend," Laurie said. "The teacher's friend told Charles to touch his toes like I just did and Charles kicked him."

38   "What are they going to do about Charles, do you suppose?" Laurie's father asked him.

Based on your school experience, what do you think they'll do with Charles?

39   "Throw him out of school, I guess," he said.

during story hour and hit a boy in the stomach and made him cry. On Friday Charles stayed after school again and so did all the other children.

41   With the third week of kindergarten Charles was an **institution** in our family; the baby was being a Charles when she cried all afternoon; Laurie did a Charles when he filled his wagon full of mud and pulled it through the kitchen; even my husband, when he caught his elbow in the telephone cord and pulled telephone, ashtray, and a bowl of flowers off the table, said, after the first minute, "Looks like Charles."

42   During the third and fourth weeks it looked like a reformation in Charles; Laurie reported grimly at lunch on Thursday of the third week, "Charles was so good today the teacher gave him an apple."

43   "What?" I said, and my husband added warily, "You mean Charles?"

44   "Charles," Laurie said. "He gave the crayons around and he picked up the books afterward and the teacher said he was her helper."

45   "What happened?" I asked incredulously.

46   "He was her helper, that's all," Laurie said, and shrugged.

> Why might Charles have changed?

47   "Can this be true, about Charles?" I asked my husband that night. "Can something like this happen?"

48   "Wait and see," my husband said cynically. "When you've got a Charles to deal with, this may mean he's only plotting."

49   He seemed to be wrong. For over a week Charles was the teacher's helper; each day he handed things out and he picked things up; no one had to stay after school.

50   "The P.T.A. meeting's next week again," I told my husband one evening. "I'm going to find Charles's mother there."

51   "Ask her what happened to Charles," my husband said. "I'd like to know."

52   "I'd like to know myself," I said.

continued

Charles continued

53   On Friday of that week things were back to normal. "You know what Charles did today?" Laurie demanded at the lunch table, in a voice slightly awed. "He told a little girl to say a word and she said it and the teacher washed her mouth out with soap and Charles laughed."

54   "What word?" his father asked unwisely, and Laurie said, "I'll have to whisper it to you, it's so bad." He got down off his chair and went around to his father. His father bent his head down and Laurie whispered joyfully. His father's eyes widened.

55   "Did Charles tell the little girl to say *that*?" he asked respectfully.

56   "She said it *twice*," Laurie said. "Charles told her to say it *twice*."

> Why might Laurie know so much about Charles?

57   "What happened to Charles?" my husband asked.

58   "Nothing," Laurie said. "He was passing out the crayons."

59   Monday morning Charles abandoned the little girl and said the evil word himself three or four times, getting his mouth washed out with soap each time. He also threw chalk.

60   My husband came to the door with me that evening as I set out for the P.T.A. meeting.

61   "Invite her over for a cup of tea after the meeting," he said. "I want to get a look at her."

62   "If only she's there," I said prayerfully.

63   "She'll be there," my husband said. "I don't see how they could hold a P.T.A. meeting without Charles's mother."

64   At the meeting I sat restlessly, scanning each comfortable matronly face, trying to determine which one hid the secret of Charles. None of them looked to me haggard enough. No one stood up in the meeting and apologized for the way her son had been acting. No one mentioned Charles.

65   After the meeting I identified and sought out Laurie's kindergarten teacher. She had a plate with a cup of tea and a piece of chocolate cake; I had a plate with a cup of tea and a piece of marshmallow cake. We maneuvered up to one another cautiously, and smiled.

66   "I've been so anxious to meet you," I said. "I'm Laurie's mother."

67   "We're all so interested in Laurie," she said.

68   "Well, he certainly likes kindergarten," I said. "He talks about it all the time."

69   "We had a little trouble adjusting, the first week or so," she said primly, "but now he's a fine little helper. With occasional lapses, of course."

70   "Laurie usually adjusts very quickly," I said. "I suppose this time it's Charles's influence."

71   "Charles?"

72   "Yes," I said, laughing, "you must have your hands full in that kindergarten, with Charles."

73   "Charles?" she said. "We don't have any Charles in the kindergarten."

Make Sense of Words Reread paragraph 41 paying close attention to the word **institution**. There are many clues in the text to help you know what **institution** means. Complete the following graphic to determine what **institution** means from the context.

institution

Context Clues

1._____

2._____

3._____

Conclusion as to what *institution* means

_____

_____

_____

_____

_____

_____

_____

Now look back at the other words you marked in the text. Can you use this vocabulary strategy to help you figure out the meanings of those words?

Read with Understanding "Charles" is clearly the main character of this short story by Shirley Jackson. As you read, you learned what Charles did, what Charles said, and how others interacted with and reacted to him. However, at the end of the story, the teacher tells Laurie's mother that there is no Charles in the kindergarten class. As you think about the ending of the story, what do you think it means?

① The teacher is lying to Laurie's mother.

② Laurie is Charles.

③ Charles is really in first grade.

④ Laurie got Charles's name wrong.

Understand by Seeing It We learn a lot about what "Charles" does through Laurie's descriptions to his parents. We get to know characters by what they say, what they do, and how other characters react to them. Fill in the chart below, *characterizing* "Charles."

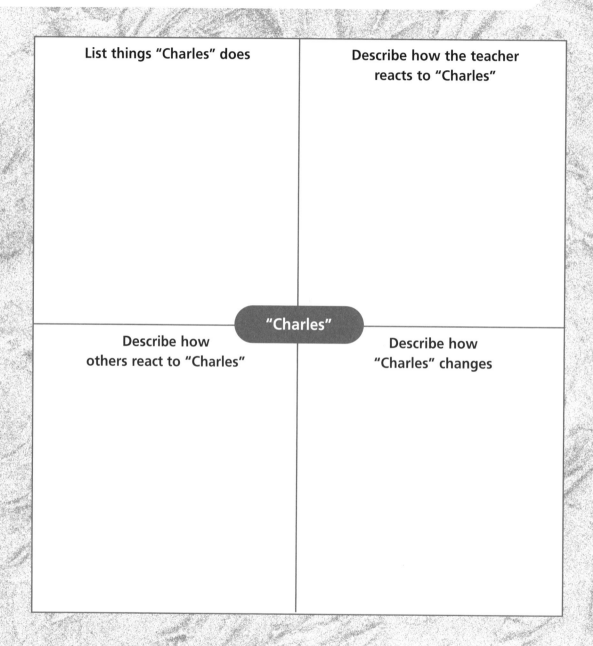

List things "Charles" does

Describe how the teacher reacts to "Charles"

"Charles"

Describe how others react to "Charles"

Describe how "Charles" changes

Write to Learn By this time, you should have figured out who "Charles" is. Why do you think Laurie created "Charles"? Why do you think "Charles" acted the way he did? Pretend that you are the school counselor and have found out about Laurie's behavior. Write a report of your opinion as to why Laurie acted the way he did and what can be done about his behavior.

Lesson 11

The Road Not Taken

• *Poem*

Heads Up As you read, you focus on the plot of the story—what is happening. *Themes* are more than just what happens. Themes are the ideas, morals, or lessons that you find within a text. A theme is a message that the author wants you to find while reading. Poems often contain themes.

Poems can seem intimidating if you don't know how to approach them. It helps your understanding if you first do a quick "preview" of the poem. Quickly glance through the poem on page 109, taking note of the title first. Make sure to also look for any repeated words or phrases. Notice what the first and last lines say. Then fill in the chart below.

Title
Repeated words or phrases
First line
Last line

As you read "The Road Not Taken," begin to think about the deeper message the author wants you to discover. The Think-Along Questions will help you focus. Also, as you read, circle or highlight any words you don't know.

The Road Not Taken

by Robert Frost

1   Two roads **diverged** in a yellow wood,
    And sorry I could not travel both
    And be one traveler, long I stood
    And looked down one as far as I could
    To where it bent in the undergrowth;

What do you think the author is considering at this point?
Predict what you think the author wants the two roads to represent.

2   Then took the other, as just as fair,
    And having perhaps the better claim,
    Because it was grassy and wanted wear;
    Though as for that the passing there
    Had worn them really about the same,

What might it mean that the road "wanted wear"?

3   And both that morning equally lay
    In leaves no step had trodden black.
    Oh, I kept the first for another day!
    Yet knowing how way leads on to way,
    I doubted if I should ever come back.

Why might the author think he would never again have
the chance to try the road he didn't choose?

4   I shall be telling this with a sigh
    Somewhere ages and ages hence:
    Two roads **diverged** in a wood, and I—
    I took the one less traveled by,
    And that has made all the difference.

What questions might you ask the author about why he chose
the road he did? Think of a time when you had a choice to make.
How did you make your decision?

Make Sense of Words Poems, especially those that are not very long, rely on their words to accomplish the purpose of the poem—to entertain, to make readers think a certain way, or to make readers feel an emotion. Obviously, words are then chosen deliberately and with much thought. The word **diverged** shows up twice in this fairly short poem, once at the beginning and once at the end. Below, define **diverged**. Then list three synonyms that Frost could have used instead. Finally, write why you think he chose **diverged**.

Two roads **diverged** in a yellow wood, and I—
I took the one less traveled by,
And that has made all the difference.

Definition of **diverged**

Synonyms Frost could have used instead

Why do you think Frost chose **diverged**?

_____

_____

_____

_____

Read with Understanding *Theme* within a piece of writing is the author's message. It is most often implied rather than stated directly. Choose the statement that best describes one possible theme for "The Road Not Taken."

① Some roads are long and hard.

② Sometimes it is best to make the less popular choice.

③ We can never change our mind about our choices.

④ We will always make the right choice.

Understand by Seeing It Think about what you have learned about *theme*. Remember, the theme is the author's implied message. State the theme of "The Road Not Taken" in your own words in "The author's message" box below. Then think about the information provided in the poem that pointed you to the author's message. Complete the graphic organizer below. An example has been provided for you.

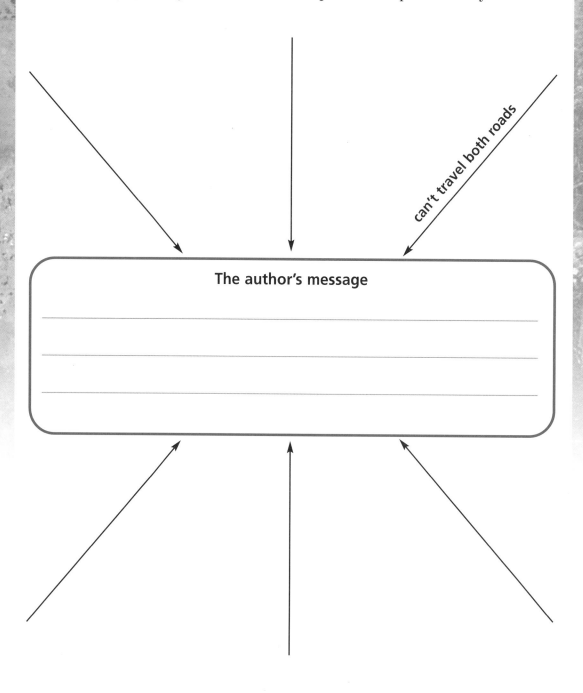

can't travel both roads

The author's message

Write to Learn Think of an experience you've had that relates to the *theme* of "The Road Not Taken." Then "interview" yourself. Ask yourself two or three interview questions to share that experience and how it fits in with the theme of the poem. Write the interview questions and your answers below.

Lesson 12

The Gift of the **Magi**

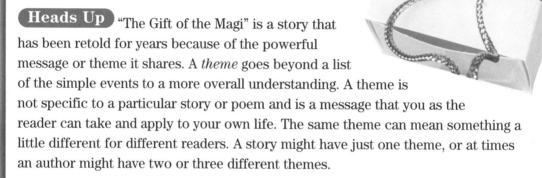

• *Short Story*

Heads Up "The Gift of the Magi" is a story that has been retold for years because of the powerful message or theme it shares. A *theme* goes beyond a list of the simple events to a more overall understanding. A theme is not specific to a particular story or poem and is a message that you as the reader can take and apply to your own life. The same theme can mean something a little different for different readers. A story might have just one theme, or at times an author might have two or three different themes.

The word *Magi* in the title might not be a familiar term. *Magi* is the term used in the Christian religion to identify wise men who followed a star to Bethlehem to bring gifts to the infant Jesus. As you think about the word *gift* and the word *Magi*, what message might the author be trying to provide for this story? Make a prediction of a possible theme, first only thinking of the word *gift*, then thinking of the word *Magi*, and finally thinking of both words together.

Word	Possible theme
gift	
Magi	
gift & Magi	

Did it change your prediction when you thought of the words separately and then together?

_____

_____

_____

_____

_____

_____

_____

Think about the author's message as you read the story and answer the Think-Along Questions. Also, as you read, circle or highlight any words you don't know.

The Gift of the **Magi**

by O. Henry • retold by Peg Hall

1   Only $1.87. That was all. And 60 cents of it was in pennies. Pennies saved one and two at a time. Saved by buying old vegetables and stale bread.

2   Three times Della counted the money. Still $1.87. And tomorrow would be Christmas. There was nothing to do but flop down on the **shabby** couch and weep. So Della did it. Which makes you think that life is made up of tears and smiles. But mostly tears.

3   While the lady of the house is getting over her sadness, let's take a look at her home. She lived in a rented flat for $8 a week. It wasn't unbearable, but it wasn't very good either.

4   In the entryway below, there was a letter box. It was too small to hold a letter. There was also a doorbell. But it didn't work. Above the doorbell was a card that read "Mr. James Dillingham Young."

5   The "Dillingham" part had seemed fine when its owner was making $30 a week. Now that he wasn't, the letters looked blurred. It was as if they were thinking of shrinking and becoming just a "D." But every time Mr. James Dillingham Young came home, he was called "Jim." And he was hugged by Mrs. James Dillingham Young. You have already met her as Della.

> What do you already know about Della?

6   Now Della finished her cry. She looked out the window. A gray cat was walking on a gray fence in a gray backyard. Tomorrow was Christmas Day. And she only had $1.87 for Jim's gift. She had been saving for months, but $20 a week doesn't go far. Things like food and rent cost a lot. So she only had $1.87 to buy a present for Jim. Her Jim.

> What do you predict she will buy for him?

7   She had spent many happy hours planning what to get him. Something fine and **rare** and silver. Something good enough to belong to Jim. Suddenly Della turned and looked into a mirror that hung on the wall. Her eyes were shining, but her face was white. She pulled the pins out of her hair and let it hang down.

8   There were two things that James Dillingham Young looked upon with pride. One was his gold watch. It had belonged to his father and grandfather. The other was Della's hair. To Jim, both were treasures. The gold watch was fine enough for a king. And Della's hair was more beautiful than any queen's could be.

9   Now Della's hair fell about her like a shiny brown waterfall. It reached below her knees and covered her like a cloak.

10   Then Della quickly pinned her hair back on top of her head. When she was done, she stood in the middle of the room for a moment. A tear or two splashed on the worn old rug.

Why would looking at her hair make Della cry?

11   On went her old brown jacket. On went her old brown hat. With a whirl of skirts, she went out the door. She hurried down the stairs to the street.

12   Della didn't stop until she reached a small shop. A sign outside said "Madame Sophia. Hair Goods of All Kinds." Della almost ran into the shop, where a tall, white-faced woman waited. She hardly looked like a "Sophia."

13   "Will you buy my hair?" asked Della.

14   "I do buy hair," said Madam. "Take off your hat, and let's have a look at it."

15   Off went the hat. Down went the shiny waterfall of hair.

16   "Twenty dollars," said Madam.

17   "Give it to me quick," said Della.

18   Oh, the next two hours flew by on **rosy** wings. Della went from shop to shop, looking for the perfect gift.

19   She found it at last. She was sure that it had been made for Jim and no one else. It was a watch chain. It had a simple, **elegant** design that spoke of value—as is true of all good things. It was worthy of Jim's watch. As soon as she saw it, Della knew it had to be Jim's.

20   Twenty-one dollars was what it cost. Della paid for it and hurried home with the 87 cents. With that chain on his watch, Jim would be proud to check the time anywhere. Grand as the watch was, he sometimes kept it out of sight. The old leather strap he used in place of a chain was worn and ugly.

continued

My Thoughts

With the information you already have, predict the author's message.

21   When Della got home, her excitement gave way to reason. She had to do something about her hacked-off hair. She heated her curling irons and went to work. She had to repair the damages done in the name of love. Which is always a big **task**, my friends. A huge task.

22   Within 40 minutes her head was covered with tiny curls. They made her look something like a schoolboy. She checked herself in the mirror.

23   "I hope Jim doesn't get mad when he first sees me," she said. "I think I look rather like a chorus girl. But what else could I do? I couldn't buy him a thing with $1.87!"

24   At 7:00 the coffee was made. The frying pan was at the back of the stove. It was hot and ready to cook the pork chops.

25   Jim was never late. Della hid the watch chain in her hand. She sat on the corner of the table near the door. Then she heard his footsteps down below. She turned white for just a moment. "Please let him think I am still pretty," she said to herself.

26   The door opened and Jim stepped in. He looked thin and very serious. Poor fellow—he was only 22. So young to have a family! He had no overcoat and no gloves.

27   Jim stopped at the door like a dog that had scented a game bird. His eyes were on Della. There was a look in them that she couldn't read. A look that frightened her. It wasn't anger, or surprise, or horror, or anything she had thought it might be. He simply stared at her with a strange expression on his face.

28   Della slid off the table and went to him. "Jim, darling," she cried, "don't look at me that way. I had my hair cut off because I wanted to buy you a gift. You don't mind, do you? I just had to do it. My hair grows fast, you know. So say 'Merry Christmas,' and let's be happy. You have no idea what a wonderful gift I have for you."

29   "You cut off your hair?" asked Jim. He asked the question as if he didn't already know the answer.

30   "Cut it off and sold it," said Della. "Don't you like me just as well, anyhow? It's still me, after all."

31   Jim looked around the room. "You say your hair is gone?"

Why would Jim react that way?

32   "There's no reason to look for it here," said Della. "It's gone, I tell you. I sold it. Now, it's Christmas Eve. Be nice to me. I sold it for you."

33   Then a sweet look came over her face. "My hair may be gone, Jim, but nobody could take my love for you."

34   Jim seemed to wake up. He put his arms around Della. For ten seconds, let us leave them alone and look in the other direction. Eight dollars a week or a million a year. What's the difference?

35   Now Jim pulled a package from his pocket and put it on the table. "Don't get me wrong, Della," he said. "Nothing you did to your hair could make me love you less. But if you unwrap that package, you'll see why you had me going."

36   Della tore at the paper and string with white fingers. When she saw what was inside, she gave a cry of joy. And then, alas! A quick change to weeping and wailing. Jim had to use all his powers to comfort her.

37   For there lay a set of hair combs. Combs that Della had often looked at in a shop window. Beautiful combs with jeweled rims. Just the thing to wear in her long, lovely hair. They cost a lot, she knew. She had looked at them without ever thinking she could own them. And now, they were hers. But she had no long hair to put them in.

Have you ever done something for someone else that people viewed as being very generous?

38   Still, she hugged the combs to her. At last she looked up at Jim and smiled. "My hair grows so fast, Jim," she said.

39   Then Della jumped up, saying, "Oh, oh!" Jim hadn't seen his beautiful present. She held it out to him on her hand. The dull metal seemed to reflect her smile.

40   "Isn't it wonderful, Jim? I hunted all over town to find it. You'll have to check the time a hundred times a day now. Give me your watch. I want to see how it looks with the chain."

continued

41   Instead of giving her the watch, Jim sank down on the couch. "Della, let's put our gifts away for a while. They're too nice to use right now. I sold the watch to get the money to buy the combs. And now, let's eat dinner."

42   The Magi, as you know, were wise men. They brought gifts to the baby in the manger. They invented the art of giving Christmas gifts. Being wise, they probably gave wise gifts. And here I have told you a tale of two foolish young people. They both unwisely gave up their greatest treasures. But here is a last word to the wise. Let it be said that of all who give and receive gifts, Della and Jim were the wisest. They are the Magi.

Make Sense of Words *Synonyms* are words having the same, or nearly the same, meaning as another word. Sometimes an author will choose a word that he or she feels is more colorful or descriptive than a more common word. Thinking about the more common synonym can help you better understand and remember unfamiliar words. Read the words below and their meanings. Then identify a synonym that might possibly be used instead.

Vocabulary word	Meaning	Synonym
shabby (¶2)	threadbare and faded from wear	
rare (¶7)	seldom occurring or found	
rosy (¶18)	tending to produce happy thoughts	
elegant (¶19)	of a high grade or quality	
task (¶21)	something hard or unpleasant that has to be done	

Now look back at the other words you marked in the text. Can you use this vocabulary strategy to help you figure out the meanings of those words?

Read with Understanding Look back to your predictions in the Heads Up section. Based on your predictions and what you now know after reading the text, which statement do you think is most closely related to the *theme*?

① Della and Jim have a happy marriage.

② It is better to give a gift than to receive one.

③ Selfish people are often punished.

④ Della and Jim competed to give the best gift.

Understand by Seeing It As you focus on *theme*, think about how O. Henry portrayed his message in "The Gift of the Magi." Remember, the theme is not a list of events but the deep, overall message from the author. Write the theme in your own words in the box below. After determining the theme, identify words, phrases, or events from the text that support your theme.

Theme

Examples that support the theme
1.
2.
3.
4.

Write to Learn After completing the information about the *theme*, think about the message the author was sharing. This seems like a theme that could be found in many different types of stories. Write a synopsis of an episode of your favorite TV show that would illustrate the same theme as "The Gift of the Magi."

The Lottery Ticket

• *Short Story*

Heads Up "The Lottery Ticket" is a story based on the thought "what if?" Ivan Dmitritch and his wife Masha think they might have won a large amount of money with the lottery ticket Masha purchased. After realizing that some of the numbers match, they decide to imagine life with lots of money before they actually look to see if they have truly won or not.

As you read this story, you need to be thinking about the reading strategies you have worked on throughout the stories in this section. These strategies include *making inferences*, *understanding characterization*, and *examining theme*. All three strategies will be important in understanding this story. Your understanding of characterization will will help you determine the critical traits evident in both Ivan and Masha and help you infer why they make the choices they do. Your inference skills will also be needed to determine what each character is really thinking as well as the story's ending. Examining the story for its theme will further aid your understanding.

continued

To begin your focus on the story, write in the space below what you would do if you were to win a large amount of money in the lottery. Would you change? Why or why not?

What I Would Do

_____

_____

_____

_____

_____

_____

_____

_____

_____

As a strategic reader you will ask yourself questions before and during reading. Sometimes the questions will help you predict what might happen, and at other times they will help you clarify what is happening or make a connection to enhance understanding.

As you read this short story, there will be times you will be asked to stop and write about your thinking or any questions you have. Record your thoughts to the Think-Along Questions in the column beside each question.

The Lottery Ticket

by Anton Chekhov • retold by Paula J. Reece

My Thoughts

1   Ivan Dmitritch was a middle-class man. He lived with his family on an income of 1200 rubles a year. And he was very well satisfied with his life.

2   One evening he was sitting on the sofa after supper. He began reading the newspaper. Then his wife Masha interrupted him.

3   "I forgot to look in the newspaper today," she said. "See if the list of lottery drawings is there."

4   Ivan looked in the paper and found the list. "Here it is," he said. "But hasn't your ticket expired?"

5   "No," his wife answered, "I just bought it on Tuesday."

> **What prediction can you make about the story?**

6   "What is the number?" Ivan asked.

7   "It is in series 9499," Masha answered. "Number 26."

8   "All right, I'll look," said Ivan. He scanned the list of drawings. "You said 9499 and 26?"

9   "Yes," said his wife nervously.

10   Ivan Dmitritch had no faith in the luck of the lottery. And he wouldn't normally agree to look at the list of winning numbers. But presently he had nothing else to do. And the newspaper was right in front of his eyes. So he passed his finger downward along the column of numbers.

11   And it was as though luck was mocking his disbelief. Because almost immediately, at the second line from the top, his eye was caught by the figure 9499!

12   Ivan couldn't believe his eyes! He quickly dropped the paper to his knees. He felt an agreeable chill in the pit of his stomach—tingling and terrible and sweet!

13   "Masha, 9499 is there!" he said in a hollow voice.

14   His wife looked at his face. It was astonished and filled with panic. She realized he was not joking.

15   "Are you sure—9499?" Masha asked. Her face turned pale. She dropped the tablecloth she'd been folding.

16   "Yes, yes—it really is there!" Ivan cried.

continued

My Thoughts

The Lottery Ticket continued

17   "What's the number of the ticket?" Masha asked.

18   "Oh, yes, there's the number of the ticket too," said Ivan. "But . . . wait! Anyway, the series of our ticket is there! You understand . . ."

> What do you need clarified so far? What questions do you have?

19   Ivan looked at his wife. And he gave her a broad, senseless smile. Like when a baby is shown a bright object.

20   Ivan's wife smiled too. Both of them were pleased that he had only mentioned the series. That he hadn't tried to find out the number of the winning ticket. How sweet and thrilling to think of the possibility of winning!

21   After a long silence, Ivan spoke again. "It is our series," he said. "So there is a reasonable chance we have won. It's only a chance, but it is there!"

22   "Well, go ahead and look!" said Masha.

23   "Wait a little," advised Ivan. "We have plenty of time to be disappointed. It's on the second line from the top, so the prize is 75,000 rubles. That's not just money—it's power! In a minute I will look at the list, and—what if we really have won?"

24   The husband and wife began laughing. They stared at each other in silence. The possibility of winning stunned them. They couldn't think about what they could use the 75,000 for. They couldn't dream of the happiness it would bring. They could only think of the figures 9499 and 75,000 and picture them in their imaginations.

25   "If we have won," he said, "it will be a new life! Of course, the ticket is yours. But if it were mine, I would, first of all, spend 25,000 on an estate. I would spend 10,000 on new furnishings, traveling, paying debts, and so on. I would put the other 40,000 in the bank to gain interest."

> How can you connect this to your own life?

26   "Yes, an estate would be nice," his wife said as she sat down. She dropped her hands in her lap.

27   Pictures crowded in Ivan's imagination. Each one was better than the last!

28   Ivan saw himself as well-fed, relaxed, and healthy . . .

29   He would be someplace warm—no, hot! He would lie on his back on the burning sand close to a stream. Or maybe he would be in the garden under a lime tree. His little boy and girl would be crawling around, digging in the sand or catching ladybugs in the grass.

30   Ivan would doze sweetly. He would think of nothing. Never would he need to go to the office—not today, tomorrow, or the day after. When the sun set he would take a long, hot bath. Then he would have tea with cream and rolls. In the evening he would take a walk or visit his neighbors.

31   "Yes, it would be nice to buy an estate," his wife said, interrupting his thoughts. It was evident by her face that she was also dreaming.

32   Ivan then pictured autumn. During that season he would have to take longer walks around the garden and beside the river. He would need to get thoroughly chilled so he could have a hot drink and warm up. The children would come running from the garden. They would bring a carrot and a radish that smelled of fresh earth.

33   Then Ivan would lie stretched full length on the sofa. He would carelessly turn the pages of a magazine. Or he would cover his face with it and give in to slumber.

34   But then Ivan remembered what followed summers there— cloudy, gloomy weather. It rained day and night. The bare trees wept. The wind was damp and cold.

What inferences can you make so far?

35   The dogs, horses, and birds would all be wet and depressed. There would be nowhere to walk. One would have to instead pace up and down the room, looking out the gray window.

36   Ivan Dmitritch stopped and looked at his wife.

37   "You know, I should travel, Masha," he said.

38   And Ivan began thinking about how nice it would be in late autumn to travel to the South of France . . . to Italy . . . to India!

39   "I would certainly like to travel too," said his wife. "But look at the number of the ticket!"

continued

The Lottery Ticket continued

40   "Wait! Wait . . ." said Ivan.

41   He walked around the room and continued thinking. What if his wife really did travel? he thought. Then he could travel someplace else alone. It is pleasant to travel alone. Or in the company of light, careless women. Those who don't think and talk all the journey about their children and fret over everything.

What questions do you have now?

42   Ivan imagined his wife in the train. She would have a number of packages and bags. She would be sighing over something. Complaining that the train made her head ache and that she had spent so much money. At the stations he would always have to be running for boiling water, bread, and butter. She wouldn't eat dinner on the train because it would be too expensive.

43   She would complain about every piece of money I spent, he thought. He glanced at his wife. Besides, what would be the use of her traveling? She would shut herself up in the hotel. And she wouldn't let me out of her sight, I know!

44   Then, for the first time in his life, Ivan thought that his wife had grown elderly and plain. She always smelled like her cooking. While, on the other hand, he was still young, fresh, and healthy. He could easily marry again.

45   Yet, I will be dependent on her, he thought. I can see it now. She will lock the money up as soon as she gets it. She will look after her relations and not let me see any of the money.

46   Ivan thought of her relations. All those **wretched** brothers, sisters, aunts, and uncles would come crawling around as soon as they heard of the winning ticket. They would begin whining like beggars. They would give Ivan those oily, fake smiles.

47   Wretched, horrible people! If they were given anything, they would only ask for more. But if they were refused money, they would swear at Ivan and Masha. They would tell lies about them and wish them every kind of misfortune.

48   Then Ivan remembered his own relations. Their faces, too, now looked ugly and hateful. They are such reptiles! he thought.

49   And his wife's face, too, struck him as ugly and hateful. Anger swelled up in his heart against her.

50   She knows nothing about money, and she is so stingy, he thought. If she won it, she would give me a hundred and put the rest away under lock and key.

51   And he looked at his wife. Not with a smile now, but with hatred. She glanced at him too. Also with hatred and anger. She had her own daydreams, her own plans. She understood perfectly well what her husband's dreams were. She knew who would be the first to try to grab her winnings.

52   Her eyes seemed to scream, "It's very nice making daydreams at other's people's expense! No, don't you dare!"

Do you want to change your prediction now?

53   Her husband understood her look. Hatred began stirring in his chest. In order to annoy his wife, he glanced quickly at the fourth page of the newspaper.

54   To spite her, he read out in triumph, "Series 9499, number 46! Not 26!"

55   Hatred and hope both disappeared instantly. At once Ivan Dmitritch and his wife thought that their house was small and dark. That the supper they had been eating was not doing them good. But instead it was lying heavy on their stomachs. That the evenings were long and wearisome . . .

56   "What the devil's the meaning of it?" asked Ivan, beginning to be in a bad mood. "Wherever one steps there are bits of paper under one's feet. Crumbs, husks. The rooms are never swept! One is simply forced to go out. I condemn my soul! I should just go hang myself on the first aspen tree!"

What are your thoughts as you finish the story?

Read with Understanding Thinking about what you have read, select the best answer for each of the following questions.

1. Ivan changes because
   Ⓐ Masha isn't nice.
   Ⓑ he finally has money.
   Ⓒ he has become greedy.
   Ⓓ he doesn't like to work.

2. Masha could best be described as
   Ⓐ a terrible wife.
   Ⓑ a woman without dreams.
   Ⓒ someone who believes in chance.
   Ⓓ a very selfish woman.

3. The best theme for this story is
   Ⓐ "All people will become corrupt if they win money."
   Ⓑ "There are things in life more important than money."
   Ⓒ "Money changes people."
   Ⓓ "It is best not to buy lottery tickets."

4. Using context clues, which do you believe is the best definition for **wretched**, found in paragraph 46?
   Ⓐ unworthy
   Ⓑ wrecked
   Ⓒ deserving
   Ⓓ beloved

Understand by Seeing It Characters often change as you read a story. It's important to pay attention not only to how a character changes, but what caused the character to change as well. This can lead you to some conclusions about the author's intended message. Fill in the chart below for both Masha and Ivan. Describe both characters at the beginning of the story and at the end of the story. In the center bubbles, describe the cause of each character's change.

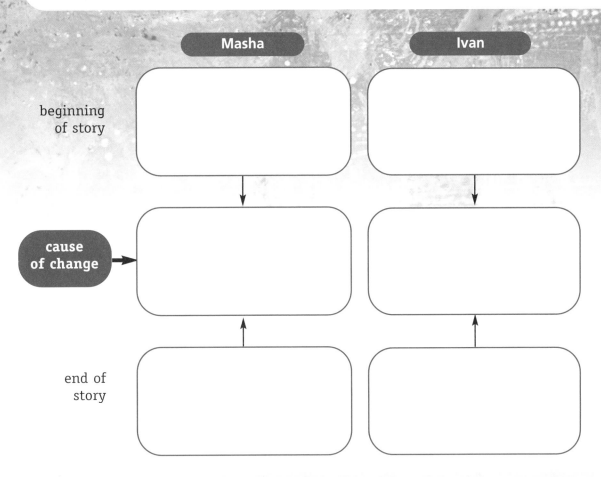

Masha

Ivan

beginning of story

cause of change

end of story

What purpose did the author have for making these characters change? What message was this supposed to give to the reader?

The Killer

• Short Story

Listening comprehension is a valuable skill. Learning and practicing good listening skills will be helpful to you in your life inside and outside of school. When you listen, it is important to sit quietly and focus your attention on the speaker.

Listen as your teacher reads the story "The Killer." Your teacher will stop about halfway through and ask you to make a prediction by answering the first question below.

1. Who do you think the killer is?

_____

After your teacher finishes reading "The Killer," answer the second question below.

2. What was the surprise in the story?

_____

_____

Now your teacher will read "The Killer" again. Listen carefully and answer the question below.

3. What clues did the author use that were misleading?

Acknowledgments

"All Together Now" by Barbara Jordan. Used by permission of Rose Mary McGowan.

"Charles" from *The Lottery and Other Stories* by Shirley Jackson. Copyright © 1948, 1949 by Shirley Jackson. Copyright renewed 1976, 1977 by Laurence Hyman, Barry Hyman, Mrs. Sarah Webster, and Mrs. Joanne Schnurer. Reprinted by permission of Farrar, Straus & Giroux, LLC.

"I've Got Your Number" by Robe Imbriano. Originally published in *The New York Times*, March 4, 1990.

"This Girl Gets Her Kicks" by Rick Reilly from *Sports Illustrated*, October 19, 1998. Reprinted courtesy of *Sports Illustrated*. Copyright © 1998, Time Inc. All rights reserved.

"This Way Nobody Gets the Blame" by Lesley Grant-Adamson. Used by permission of the author.